Preface

The growing number of courses which include Workshop Technology has resulted in a remarkable increase in the number of students who are now required to answer descriptive questions on this important aspect of engineering. The author has had many years' experience in examining, and is convinced that the greater proportion of candidates rarely do themselves justice. An examiner can only award marks for information provided by the candidate. He can make no allowance whatever for knowledge the candidate possesses but does not communicate. The main purpose of this volume is to guide students in examination technique. It is not intended to be a textbook on Workshop Technology but, in providing specimen answers, it is obvious that a considerable amount of information can be introduced which will prove valuable to the reader.

In selecting the questions, and in the scope of the answers, the author aimed at the T2 level of the Mechanical Engineering Technicians Course. Much of the syllabus content of this particular course also appears in a typical O2 syllabus, and also in the first year of a Degree course in Engineering, especially of the C.N.A.A. type, particularly if students qualify for entrance by virtue of G.C.E. 'A' Level successes. Consequently it is felt that the volume will be of use on courses other than M.E.T. T2.

It would be arrogant to suggest that the answers provided in this volume are perfect. Each answer has been submitted to a panel of experienced examiners, and their collective opinion is that high marks would be allocated for the answers provided.

The author is clearly aware that in writing this volume he is offering himself as a target for criticism. His colleagues are aware that his sympathies are inclined far more towards students than other parties. The needs of students are such that a book of this type just had to be written. He is well aware that certain answers will be criticized but, just as in the text he has earnestly requested students to distinguish between fact and opinion, he would commend this attitude to his colleagues. In particular, it must be noted that the book is intended for T2 students, and the answers must relate to their syllabus and level of learning. The book is an unusual venture in the sphere of Workshop Technology, and the author cordially invites interested readers to write to him with constructive criticisms.

The questions, in the majority of cases, have appeared on past examination papers and have been selected as far as possible to avoid duplication. In order to cover subject matter as fully as possible, in certain chapters a few questions have been specially constructed to bring out particular points. Where possible, these are based on questions which have appeared on past examination papers. In a few cases, quoted sizes have been converted into appropriate metric equivalents.

The author acknowledges the permission of examining authorities to reproduce questions from examinations conducted under their jurisdiction. (The answers provided are those of the author, and must not be interpreted as the official answers of the examining authorities, and the metric conversions have been made by the author so as not to change the relative accuracy.)

The author wishes to express his thanks to those colleagues who have read, contributed to and commented upon the specimen answers. Sincere appreciation is acknowledged of the assistance provided by Messrs. H. Matthews, D. Kendrick, W. Woodward, W. Vaughan and R. Mellor, members of the Staff of the Department of Production Engineering, Wolverhampton College of Technology. Finally, the author wishes to acknowledge the assistance rendered by Mrs. Dorothy Wilson, who patiently typed the manuscript with competence and skill.

M. G. PAGE

Wolverhampton
1969

Contents

Examination Technique

Let us review some of the important considerations in answering a typical examination paper in Workshop Technology.

Of first concern to the candidate is the appreciation of the task which confronts him. It is unusual to have examination papers in Workshop Technology other than those which permit complete freedom of choice of a stated number of questions from a greater number of questions. The questions normally have equal mark value, and the task has to be completed in a given time. This results in two important considerations of which a candidate must be clearly aware, viz:

1. It is expected that the time devoted to each question should be reasonably constant. In an examination lasting three hours in which a candidate has to answer six questions, after allowing for reading of questions, filling in title sheets and a revision of answers, the examiner is aware that approximately twenty-five minutes is available for each question. A candidate may feel that an answer can be provided in a few minutes of work or, alternatively, that his knowledge is of such a range that he could spend an hour or more on the question. He must appreciate that the examiner, in setting the paper, has sincerely attempted to create questions of equal mark value, and hence equal time commitment. The candidate must reflect this constraint on the examiner in the structure of his answer.

2. It is not necessary to provide perfect answers to the required number of questions in order to achieve a pass level. Most papers can be passed if a candidate answers perfectly about one-third of the *total* number of questions on the paper. Some candidates with considerable experience of examinations decide previously not to attempt certain types of question, and concentrate on but a proportion of a complete syllabus. In certain circumstances this often results in a pass, but the dangers of too drastic a limitation should be obvious. The practice may achieve a pass, but it does not substantially contribute to education in its fullest sense.

The questions on an examination paper should be read carefully, and the requirements of the examiner clearly understood.

There is often an important difference between what an examiner requests and what the candidate would like to read. An examiner can only award marks for answers to the question he has set. The author has often been confronted with essays which are accurate and well presented but unfortunately *those essays were not answers to the questions he had set*. His terms of reference were such that for some accurate and precise information he was compelled to award low, and often no, marks.

A candidate, in answering a question, has to communicate information to the examiner. In the main, but not wholly, the communication will be by the written word. There are delicate but definite differences between concise technical reporting and formal grammar, and on occasions it can be beneficial to modify the rules of grammar if substantial benefits accrue. Presenting technical information within a rigid time schedule does not lend itself to verbosity.

Candidates are recommended to use sketches freely to support their answers. Information can often be more rapidly conveyed by a suitable annotated sketch than by a lengthy essay. The savings in time by using sketches can be extremely significant. A sketch need not be freehand, or in perspective, or in some similar classically artistic form. Many sketches are satisfactory if they are line diagrams in good proportion.

In the examination room, the candidate should read the rubric (the instructions to candidates) very carefully to note what the examiner requests. He should then proceed to read the questions to form an opinion of the standard of the paper. He then has to come to grips with his own conscience and decide whether he will be satisfied with a pass or, alternatively, whether he feels that he is capable of a performance in excess of a pass, such as a 'distinction'. If the latter is the case, the allocation of time per question becomes a most important consideration, since he must now allocate approximately equal times to the questions he attempts. On the other hand, if a pass level is acceptable, it is better to spend a little extra time on the first few questions to ensure high marks, being fully aware that the answers to later questions will be used to consolidate the attempt at a pass.

In producing an answer to a question, the answer should be planned. The main points which a candidate expects to cover should be jotted down on spare paper (or on the rear pages of the answer book). These main points should then be adjusted into a logical sequence and any necessary linking decided. A candidate is advised never to commence writing until he has decided on the complete scope of his answer. Workshop Technology is mainly a factual science, but there are occasions when opinion is called into effect. A candidate should clearly distinguish between fact and opinion, selecting appropriate wording as circumstances dictate.

The method of awarding the marks, which the examining authority conveys to the examiner, ought to be communicated to candidates. It is unfortunate that authorities do not completely agree in the method of the award of marks, but the majority follow a standard procedure. Examiners, in general, award marks according to agreed schemes. If only part of a question has been answered the examiner will usually award a proportion of the total marks. If a candidate cannot answer fully the required number of questions he should attempt as many parts of questions that he can. If a candidate answers more than the required number of questions, most examiners are instructed to mark every question, but obtain a total after discounting the lowest marks. For instance, if a candidate is instructed to answer six questions, but attempts eight, the examiner will probably be instructed to mark all eight, but the total mark will be obtained from the best six individual marks. It is surprising to note that even now some examiners are instructed to discount completely the later questions if more than the required number have been attempted. If the examination consists of written answers on loose-leaf paper with added drawings and graphs, one wonders how the examiner decides the order in which questions were answered. The author feels most strongly that candidates in an examination ought to be aware of the attitude of the examiner on the marking of excess questions, and suggests that students ask their teachers to obtain this information for them.

Candidates are advised to strike out clearly any information they do not wish the examiner to consider. Such striking-out should not be undertaken rashly, and a candidate should be particularly careful that the striking-out does not include information which really should be left in.

Finally, the majority of the questions in this book have already appeared on examination papers so it is extremely improbable that identical questions will ever appear again. The reader is therefore recommended not to use this volume as a textbook. Excellent textbooks are available, and natural evolution will bring out better textbooks. A typical Workshop Technology syllabus has such wide scope that it is essential to supplement studies in the classroom, laboratory and workshop by extra reading. This volume falls into the category of 'extra reading', being specifically intended to assist the reader in examination technique. Nevertheless, it must be pointed out that there is a measure of information contained in this book which does not appear in recognized textbooks, and the author sincerely trusts the reader will profit from the acquisition of that information.

CHAPTER 1

Heat Treatment

The questions in this chapter are based mainly upon the following items of the T2 syllabus for Mechanical Engineering Technicians:

Heat treatment of plain carbon steels; hardening, tempering, normalizing and annealing; simple consideration of change points and internal structure; surface hardening by pack and salt bath methods.
Temperature measurement by thermometer and thermocouple instruments.
Construction and use of simple muffle and salt-bath furnaces; fuels and temperatures used.
Hardness and impact tests.

1.1 **Describe how a 0·87 per cent carbon steel 12 mm diameter should be heat treated to obtain the following conditions:**
(a) as hard as possible;
(b) as soft as possible;
(c) as tough as possible;
(d) in the best condition for machining. (U.E.I.)

A steel with a carbon content of 0·87% can be assumed to have eutectoid composition. There is no critical range, the upper and lower critical points are coincident, in the close vicinity of 720°C. In the following heat treatments it is assumed that in every case the steel is 'soaked' to achieve a uniform temperature throughout its mass.

(a) The steel should be subjected to a full-hardening heat treatment by heating to between 730°C and 740°C, followed by quenching vertically in circulating brine in order to obtain the fastest possible cooling rate. This will result in the formation of the greatest possible amount of martensite.

(b) The steel should be subjected to a full-annealing heat treatment by heating to a temperature of 730°C to 740°C and cooling at the

1

slowest possible rate. Two common methods are by cooling down in the furnace or by burying in ashes. The slow cooling produces the softest structure, in this case it will be of pearlite.

(c) The tough condition is obtained by first subjecting the steel to the hardening, as in **(a)**, followed as soon as possible by a 'tempering' heat treatment. Tempering increases toughness by sacrificing some of the hardness. 'As tough as possible' must be interpreted in relation to the intended use of the steel. The steel, after hardening, should be heated within the range of 200°C to 400°C, greater toughnesses occurring in the higher portion of the range. Cooling is a matter of opinion, the rate is not really critical, the majority favouring cooling in oil.

(d) The softest possible state is not necessarily the best possible condition for machining. To facilitate machining, the steel should allow chip cracks to propagate, and in this case the steel should be subjected to a normalizing heat treatment. The steel would be heated to between 770°C and 820°C and cooled freely in air, away from draughts.

1.2   A piece of 0·6 per cent carbon steel is heated slowly to slightly above the upper critical temperature and quenched in water. Explain, using a carbon equilibrium diagram, the changes which occur in the structure of the material during the stages through which it passes.

(U.E.I.)

The simplified iron-carbon equilibrium diagram for plain carbon steels is sketched in Fig. 1.2, the percentages of carbon and the temperatures being approximate. At room temperature, in its soft condition, a 0·6% plain carbon steel has a structure of about two-thirds of pearlite and one-third of ferrite (point A). As the temperature is gradually raised, at about 720°C the pearlite starts to go into solid solution with the ferrite, which by now is in the gamma-iron phase (point B). Within the range of about 720°C to about 780°C the structure gradually transforms to austenite, which is a solid solution of iron-carbide in gamma-iron (points B to C). At temperatures in excess of about 780°C the structure is austenitic (point D). If the 0·6% plain carbon steel is quenched in water from a temperature slightly above 780°C, the steel is cooled at a rate faster than its critical cooling rate, and the structural transformation indicated by line DCBA is prevented. Instead, a hard needle-like

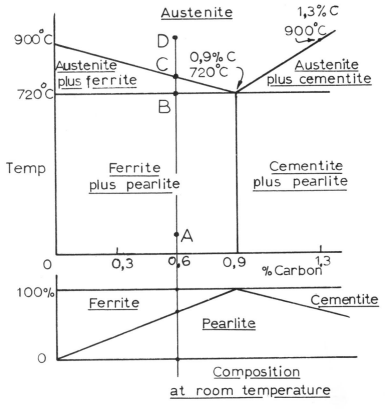

Fig. 1.2

constituent called martensite appears in the structure; this makes the steel harder. At room temperature, the structure would be mainly martensite plus ferrite.

Note on the simplified iron-carbon diagram for plain carbon steels: The general shape of the diagram should be accepted by most examiners at the stage of studies for which this book was intended. The temperatures and percentages of carbon are approximate but lend themselves to rapid construction of the diagram. There are differences of opinion, even among reputable authorities, for the percentage composition of eutectoid steel and the corresponding temperature on the diagram. Values quoted range from 0·8% to 0·9% carbon, and from 700°C to 730°C, the greater body of opinion favour-

3

ing 0·87% carbon at 723°C. The values used on the diagram will not create significant errors with the usual type of question expected at this stage. If a question quotes a carbon content of 0·8% to 0·9%, this should be interpreted as eutectoid steel.

The reader should carefully note that the structural changes indicated only occur with very slow heating and cooling. The diagram does not explain *what happens with rapid quenching.*

1.3(a) What is meant by the following terms used in the heat treatment of plain carbon steels: (i) arrest points; (ii) austenite; (iii) martensite? (b) Make a sketch of the type of furnace in common use for the heat treatment of steel. Indicate the internal details by a cross-section and describe its operation and use. (N.C.T.E.C.)

(a) (i) If heat is being applied to a body, the temperature rises unless there is change of state or a change in structure. If heat is being extracted, the temperature falls unless there is a change in state or a change in structure. At these changes, the rise or fall in temperature is stopped and for a period is constant, i.e. the temperature change is 'arrested'.

Arrest points are temperatures at which a change in phase occurs. In the heat treatment of the steels, a change from phase A to phase B occurs at a slightly different temperature from that at which phase B changes to phase A, according to whether the steel is being heated or cooled. The symbol A is used to denote an arrest point, the small letter r for heating, the small letter c for cooling, followed by a suffix number or symbols to indicate the change of phase, e.g. Ar_1, and Ac_{cm}.

The slight difference in temperature between arrest points such as Ac_1 and Ar_1 is usually neglected in preliminary studies, and an approximate single value is used. For example, with hypo-eutectoid steels, the single approximate value for Ac_1 and Ar_1 is loosely called the lower critical point and the single value for Ac_3 and Ar_3 is loosely called the upper critical point, the temperatures between these values being known as the critical range.

(ii) Austenite is the solid solution of carbide of iron in the allotropic form of iron termed gamma-iron.

(iii) Martensite is an extremely hard needle-like constituent which appears when a steel in the austenitic condition is cooled at a rate faster than its critical cooling rate.

4

(b) A furnace in common use for the heat treatment of steel is known as the gas-fired forced-draught muffle furnace, shown in Fig. 1.3a.

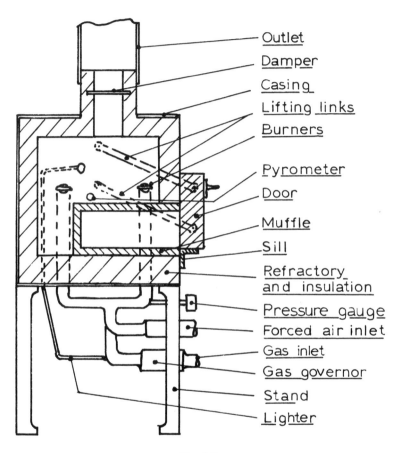

Fig. 1.3a

The burners are lit in a similar manner to a bunsen burner, i.e. gas only at first. The air is then increased, and temperature is controlled by manipulating quantities of gas and of air, together with the position of the damper. Modern furnaces link the pyrometer reading to the fuel controls to provide automatic control. The muffle protects the work from the products of combustion and minimizes scaling. If an inert gas is used in the muffle, or throughout the furnace, the furnace is termed 'controlled atmosphere'. A simple balanced drop door is lifted to provide access to the inside of the muffle and the work placed inside by tongs, resting on refractory supports. A pyrometer is used to check temperature and 'soaking' is necessary to ensure the attaining of a suitable temperature.

After a suitable time, the work is withdrawn by tongs and quenched.

Alternative solution to part (b)

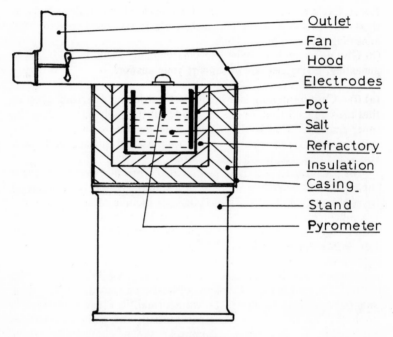

Fig. 1.3b

A furnace in common use for the heat treatment of steel is known as the electric salt bath furnace. The salt is contained in a pot made of alloy steel. The pot is surrounded by a refractory material, insulation and the casing. For quench hardening, a neutral salt is used. For surface hardening, a cyanide salt is used. Forced fume extraction is essential for the latter, natural fume exhaust is more common for the neutral salt. Heating is obtained from the action of an electric current through the salt—this action also produces a stirring effect.

Temperature is measured by a pyrometer—modern furnaces linking the reading to the electric supply to provide automatic control.

Having been carefully dried or preheated to prevent 'spitting' on immersion, articles are suspended from wires on rods across the pot and totally immersed in the salt. After immersion for a suitable soaking time they are withdrawn and quenched.

1.4(a) Explain the purpose served by each of the following heat-treatment processes on plain carbon steel: (i) case-hardening, (ii) annealing, and (iii) normalizing.

(b) Give an example to show where normalizing would be preferred to annealing, giving reasons to support your answer. (U.L.C.I.)

(a) (i) Case-hardening is a method of hardening a ferrous alloy so that the outer portion, or case, is made substantially harder than the inner portion, or core. Its purpose is to produce a material which can resist abrasion and wear due to the hard surface and resist shock loading due to the softer core.

(ii) Annealing is a heat treatment for metallic materials where the material is heated to and held at a suitable temperature followed by cooling at a suitable rate. Its purposes include softening, improving machineability, facilitating cold working, producing a desired structure, or obtaining desired mechanical, physical or other properties. When applied to ferrous materials, without qualifications, the word annealing is interpreted as 'full-annealing', involving very slow cooling, so that the material is in its softest possible state.

(iii) Normalizing is a process of heating a ferrous material to a suitable temperature above the transformation range, followed by cooling in air to a temperature substantially below the transformation range. Its purpose is to improve the machineability of the material, modify the grain structure, render the structure more uniform and to improve mechanical properties.

(b) The main reason for preferring normalizing to annealing a ferrous material is when improved machineability is desired. A material in its softest state is not necessarily in its most machineable state. To facilitate machining the material must allow chip cracks to propagate and not spread on the tool point. Annealing a ferrous material produces a soft material which may not machine as easily as a normalized material.

1.5(a) Give the temperature to which normalizing should be carried out on
  (i) **a 1 % plain carbon steel.**
  (ii) **a 0·3 % plain carbon steel.**
(b) Explain briefly the reason for the considerable difference in the above temperatures and say how the appropriate normalizing temperature for any plain carbon steel can be obtained.
(c) State two reasons for carrying out a normalizing process. (C.G.L.I.)

(a) (i) About 840°C for a 1% plain carbon steel.
  (ii) About 915°C for a 0·3% plain carbon steel.

(b) Normalizing is carried out by heating to between 50°C and 100°C above the upper critical point, followed by cooling in air. The upper critical point varies with the carbon content, hence causing the difference in the values.

For hypo-eutectoid steels (having a carbon content less than about 0·9% of carbon) the upper critical point falls approximately linearly from about 900°C to about 720°C. Hence, if $x\%$ is the percentage of carbon, the approximate value of the upper critical point is $(900 - 180x/0\cdot9)°C = (900 - 200x)°C$. Adding on a mean value of 75°C above the upper critical point, the approximate normalizing temperature for hypo-euctectoid steels is $(975 - 200x)°C$, giving 915°C for a 0·3% carbon steel.

For hyper-euctectoid steels (having a carbon content in excess of 0·9%), the upper critical point rises approximately linearly from about 720°C at about 0·9% carbon to about 900°C at 1·3% carbon. Hence if $x\%$ is the percentage of carbon, the value of the upper critical point is approximately $(315 + 450x)°C$. Adding on a mean value of 75°C gives an approximate normalizing temperature of $(390 + 450x)°C$ for hyper-eutectoid steel, producing the value of 840°C for a 1% carbon steel.

(c) Two reasons for normalizing are:
1. to refine a grain structure in steel which has been coarsened by the high temperature of forging; and
2. to produce in a steel the best possible conditions for machining.

1.6(a) Why is it important to work at accurate temperatures when heat treating steel?
(b) What is the significance of arrest (change) points in the heating of plain carbon steels?
(c) Three identical pieces of high carbon steel are heated in the same hardening temperature and quenched in water, oil and cold air respectively. What differences will be found in the pieces? (Y.C.F.E.)

(a) The range of temperature for the correct heat treating of steel can be, on many occasions, relatively very small. For example, with eutectoid steel, a difference of about 10°C can cause a difference as distinct as softness and hardness. A second example occurs with a 0·6% carbon steel. Every 10°C above the upper critical point contributes a significant amount to the degree of grain growth. A third example occurs in the tempering range, when once again a difference of 10°C causes a significant difference in the amount of toughness in the tempered steel. The relative accuracy of 10°C for the three cases quoted is an order of accuracy of about 1·5%, 1% and 3% respectively. Although the order of accuracy for some heat-treatment processes may not be as small as those quoted, muffle and similar furnaces may be used for a variety of purposes, and the order of accuracy of temperature determination must be the smallest required for the various duties. This could be as low as 1% and hence accurate determination of temperature is necessary.

(b) The arrest points occur when a change of phase occurs, and indicate when a steel starts or finishes a significant phase in the heating. As an example, with a hypo-eutectoid steel (less than about 0·9% carbon) an arrest occurs at about 720°C when the pearlite starts to go into solid solution with the ferrite. Another arrest occurs at a higher temperature—the value depending upon the carbon content—indicating that the formation of the solid solution is complete, all the pearlite having gone into solid solution, the steel then being in the austenitic condition. If quenched from this condition at a rate faster than the critical cooling rate, the steel will harden, the degree of hardness depending upon the carbon content. The arrest points are significant because they indicate boundaries of important phases.

(c) The first will be hard, and its hardness will be very close to the greatest possible degree of hardness that could be obtained. (Quenching in brine would yield a slightly harder steel.) The steel would be brittle and, if of complicated shape, may show a tendency to crack.

9

The second piece would also be hard and brittle, but not so hard or as brittle as the first piece, and there would be relatively little tendency to crack.

The third piece would not harden, it would be normalized. It would not be in the softest possible condition that could be obtained, but would have a very uniform grain size and be in the best possible condition for machining.

1.7(a) What is the object of tempering plain high carbon steel?
(b) State the temperature range within which the simple tempering of plain high carbon steel is usually carried out.
(c) Explain why it is necessary to have a range of temperature rather than a single temperature for the tempering process.
(d) State a type of furnace and method of temperature control suitable for use in tempering small batches of punches. (C.G.L.I.)

(a) The object of tempering plain high carbon steels after they have been hardened is to reduce the brittleness in hardened steel and to reduce the internal strains caused by the sudden cooling that occurs when quenching.

(b) The tempering is performed by reheating to a suitable temperature below the transformation range, followed by cooling. The reheating is usually to some temperature in the range 220°C to 340°C.

(c) Tempering sacrifices some hardness to improve toughness. The service requirements of hardened plain carbon steels calls for different balances of hardness and toughness. In general, the higher the tempering temperature, the greater the toughness. Thus cutting tools are tempered at lower temperatures, since hardness is of more importance than toughness. Conversely, a rivet set would be tempered towards the higher end of the range. A single temperature is not suitable for every usage.

(d) A suitable type of furnace would be an electrically heated neutral salt bath. A simple temperature control could be obtained by a thermostat which incorporates a bimetallic strip. The thermostat is set to 'cut-in' the electric supply to the heating elements at one temperature and to 'cut-out' the supply at a slightly higher temperature.

1.8(a) What is meant by (i) tempering, as applied to hardened high carbon steel, (ii) temper, as applied to rolled phosphor-bronze strip? **(b)** A skilled heat-treatment operator can often judge temperature by 'temper colours'. State the cause of these colours and the colours associated with particular temperatures. (U.L.C.I.)

(a) (i) Tempering, as applied to a hardened high carbon steel, is a process of reheating the hardened steel below the transformation temperature range (i.e. the critical range) followed by cooling. The purpose of tempering is to remove the internal strains caused by rapid quenching and to reduce the brittleness of the product. Some of the hardness of the steel is sacrificed to acquire greater toughness. The amount of tempering depends upon the service requirements of the hardened detail.

(ii) Temper, as applied to rolled phosphor-bronze strip, is an indication of the severity of the cold rolling which has work hardened the strip. Common indications are 'quarter hard' and 'half hard'. Temper is an indication of how the metal will react to bending and similar cold forming operations. The harder the temper the more difficult it is to perform the bending and the greater the amount of 'spring back'.

(b) If steel is heated in an oxidizing atmosphere a film of oxide forms on the surface of the steel. This oxide film changes colour with changing temperature.
Approximate temperatures associated with various colours are:

Light yellow	230°C
Straw yellow	240°C
Brown	250°C
Brown purple	260°C
Full purple	275°C
Full blue	310°C

1.9 For what reasons is case-hardening employed? Describe two different methods of carbonizing and indicate the type of component for which each is suitable. (C.G.L.I.)

Case-hardening is a heat-treatment process applied to a ferrous alloy so that the surface layer (or case) is substantially harder than the interior (or core). The process is usually applied to steels of low carbon content, and the final result is a case of wear-resistant hardened steel around a soft, ductile, shock-resistant core. The process itself gives a guide to the reasons for its use. ·

1. Hardness alone is rarely a requirement, it is more usual to require a combination of hardness and toughness. Case-hardening is one method of achieving this purpose. It provides a material which has a surface which resists abrasion and has a core which resists shock loading.

2. The process allows for 'selective' hardening; the heat treatment can be undertaken so that only certain surfaces of the component have a hard surface.

3. The process generally allows for cheaper production. The cost, both as regards basic material cost and machining cost, is lower than an alloy or high carbon steel.

4. The effect of stress-raisers such as undercuts and recesses have less effect than with a fully-hardened material. Components have less tendency to crack or distort in the heat-treatment process.

5. The heat-treatment process is less exacting. Variations in composition and temperature have less effect than with fully hardened material.

6. The case depth can be easily controlled, and the physical properties of case and core are relatively easily separately controlled.

Carbonizing (sometimes called carburizing) is the process of increasing the carbon content of the surface of a ferrous component so that with the appropriate heat treatment the surface will harden.

Two common methods are:

1. cyanide carbonizing;
2. pack carbonizing.

In the cyanide process, components are suspended in a bath of hot molten salt, which consists of 8%–15% of sodium cyanide with barium salts. Temperatures in the vicinity of 900°C are used, provided by gas or electric heating. The time in the bath depends on the case depth required.

The cyanide process finds favour because of its flexibility—parts of varied design can be accommodated simultaneously, being easily extracted at appropriate times. Case formation is rapid and it is possible on occasions to omit the refining process normally required with pack carbonizing. The type of component is generally small, is required in reasonable quantities, case depth rarely exceeds 1 mm, is usually surface-hardened all over, and is required to be 'scale free'. A typical component would be the stock of an adjustable spanner.

In the pack process, the carbonizing material is organic matter rich in animal charcoal, together with an 'activator'. A metal container is used, in which the components are carefully packed so as not to touch each other and to be surrounded by adequate carbonizing material. The temperature is the same as with the cyanide process, but since components tend to be larger, carbonizing times are longer. Gas and electric furnaces are common. The containers are sealed, and the heating of the organic matter causes a complex chemical reaction where gases carry the carbon into the steel.

The components in general are of larger size, since a cyanide pot rarely exceeds 300 mm in diameter and depth. Selective carbonizing is usually undertaken by the pack method, parts required to be soft are covered with clay or copper. Components are generally not required in large quantities, the space required for preparation and for recovery is considerable and the process is none too clean.

A typical component for pack-carbonizing would be a long shaft with one or both ends threaded, where the threads only are to be left soft.

1.10   A steel pin has to withstand considerable wear and abrasion as well as shock loads. Give the carbon content of a suitable steel and describe fully the heat treatment which will confer the desired properties. (U.L.C.I.)

A material suitable for parts which have to withstand wear, abrasion and shock loading is a case-hardened steel. The use of the word 'considerable' in the question implies the use of a better quality material than a plain carbon case-hardening steel such as En 32.

There is a range of suitable steels which include nickel. In view of limited information on the shape, size and use of the pin, a suitable material should be

5% Nickel Case-Hardening Steel (En 37)

The carbon content of this steel (before the case-hardening treatment) does not exceed 0·16%.

Heat Treatment

1. Carburize at 900°C, cool in furnace.
2. Refine at 875°C, quench. (Quenching medium unimportant: air, oil or water.)

3. Harden from 775°C, quench in oil.

Assuming the pin to be other than very small, the carbon content of the surface would be increased by pack carburizing. The article would be placed in a container surrounded by an organic carbonaceous material and sealed in the container. The container would be placed in a furnace, the temperature raised slowly to 900°C and held at this temperature. The heat causes a complex chemical reaction which increases the carbon content of the surface and thus enables the surface to be hardened. The carburizing time depends upon the depth of case required, the size of the article and the activity of the carbonaceous material. Even allowing for the nickel content, the lengthy heating at 900°C causes grain growth and, after cooling in the furnace, the grains should be brought to a smaller size by the refining treatment. This refines the core, and the final hardening and refining of the case is undertaken by heating to 775°C and quenching in oil.

1.11(a) Sketch a simple graph to show the relationship between case depth and time for a carburizing process. Using the graph explain why it is expensive to obtain a deep case.

(b) Assuming a plain carbon steel component, what would be, approximately, the composition and condition of (i) the case and (ii) the core, after carburizing?

(c) Give brief details of the heat treatment required to secure maximum core strength. What test could be applied to check the core strength?

(C.G.L.I.)

(a) A simple graph is shown in Fig. 1.11.

No scales are indicated, the time will depend mainly upon the activity of the carburizing process. The general form indicates that as the case depth increases, the time to produce a unit increase in case depth also increases and, irrespective of the carburizing medium, after a case depth of about 2 mm has been acquired the curve is almost horizontal. As the time increases, so does the cost, and although it will not necessarily increase in proportion a very deep case will prove to be very expensive.

(b) The case would have a carbon content of 0·7% to 1·2% carbon, depending upon the carburizing medium, and probably in the vicinity of eutectoid steel, about 0·9%; it would be pearlitic in structure.

The core would retain its original carbon content of about

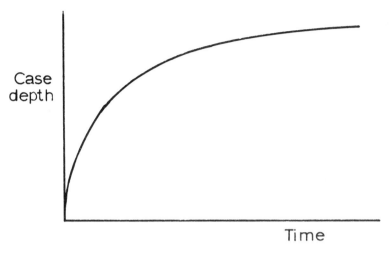

Fig. 1.11

0·2% and would have about one-quarter pearlite, the balance being ferrite.

Both the core and the case would have grains of large size, grain growth having occurred during the carburizing process.

(c) A heat treatment known as 'refining the core' would be undertaken. (The final hardening by quenching will refine the case.) The steel would be heated to about 875°C and cooled in oil or water.

No test can be applied which would check the core strength without damaging the article. It is conventional practice to insert blanks of the same material as the articles to be carburized and to subject them to carburizing and core-refining with the articles. The test piece could then be subjected to a standard tensile test to destruction.

Some additional information on the core could be obtained from an Izod test and from a metallurgical examination, but this would convey very little reliable information on 'strength'. A hardness test value bears some relation to tensile strength, but the comparison is not reliable, while the Izod test should be used to give an indication of notch-sensitivity rather than 'strength'.

15

1.12(a) Give two ways in which overheating of a steel could easily occur.

(b) State briefly what effect overheating has upon a plain carbon steel, and the temperature level at which it is most likely to develop.

(c) What part can hardness or impact tests play in detecting steel which is faulty through overheating? (C.G.L.I.)

(a) Two ways in which overheating of a steel could easily occur are:
1. Leaving the steel at too high a temperature for too long a time. Soaking time should be kept to a minimum, just sufficient to ensure the whole mass is at the required temperature. Prolonged soaking is a common cause of overheating. When an article is pack carburized the necessary soaking for a long time almost inevitably leads to overheating and the resulting grain growth.
2. Either by accidental error or by the malfunctioning of equipment, using the wrong temperature for the work in hand. A correct temperature for a process may be say 740°C. If by error an operative decided to use 780°C, or the pyrometer reading was 40°C low, overheating would occur.

(b) Overheating is the exposure of a metal to an unduly high temperature, whereby it acquires a coarse-grained structure. (Although a burnt steel has also been raised to an unduly high temperature, such a steel has been permanently damaged. The distinction between a burnt steel and an overheated steel is that an overheated steel can be corrected by a suitable heat treatment, or mechanical working, or a combination of both.)

The temperature level at which overheating is liable to occur is above the upper critical point for the composition of the steel. Grain growth associated with overheating really commences at the recrystallization temperature, but the growth that occurs between then and the upper critical point is not considered to be a defect resulting from overheating. A typical temperature at which overheating and resulting grain growth occurs is 900°C with a 0·3% plain carbon steel.

(c) The detection of overheating is based mainly upon detecting excessive grain growth. There are better ways of detecting excessive grain growth than by using hardness and impact tests, e.g. by metallurgical examination. Nevertheless, an overheated steel is softer and less resistant to impact than a steel of the same composition which has not been overheated. In any case, modern opinion does not consider an Izod or similar test to be a true impact test because the

results are closely connected with the notch. As a general consideration, it would probably be best to say that hardness and impact tests
may provide evidence to suggest overheating, but not conclusive
evidence; this must be obtained by examining the grain size and the
condition of the grain boundaries by metallurgical examination.

**1.13(a) Describe three different methods of ensuring that certain parts
of a case-hardened component may be left unhardened. Name the case-
hardening process used in each case.**

**(b) Sketch a cross-section of a round plain carbon steel bar which has
been pack carburized for six hours at 900°C, and indicate on the
sketch values for the probable case depth and carbon content of case
and core.**

**(c) Describe how the heat-treatment process would be carried out for
refining the coarse ferrite-pearlite structure of the core of the bar in (b)
after the carburizing process, quoting the heating temperature used and
the position of this temperature with respect to the critical points of the
core.** (N.C.T.E.C.)

(a) 1. Cover the parts to be left soft with clay, to prevent the active
gases generated in carburizing from contacting those parts. This
method is usually used when pack carburizing, due to the danger of
spattering from the water content of the clay.
  2. Leave surplus material on the parts which are to be left soft
and machine them away after carburizing. This method is usually
used when pack carburizing, as cyanide carburizing increases the
hardness of the skin to some extent by the formation of nitrides.
  3. Cover the parts to be left soft with copper, either by electro-
deposition or by the use of a proprietary paint based on copper
powder. This is an expensive process usually reserved for small areas
and cyanide carburizing.

(b) The sketch required is shown in Fig. 1.13. The depth of case can
vary considerably according to:
  1. the activity of the carburizing medium
  2. the size of article
  3. the condition of the surface
but a reasonable average would be 1 to 2 mm depth of case. The
case would have about 1% of carbon, while the carbon content of
the core would remain unchanged at about 0·20% maximum.

17

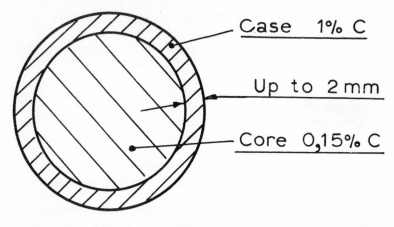

Fig. 1.13

(c) The heat-treatment process known as 'refining the core' would be carried out by heating to some temperature above the upper critical point of the steel and cooling in air, oil or water. The actual temperature depends upon the carbon content of the steel. The upper critical point is about 900°C for zero carbon and decreases by about 20°C for each 0·1% of carbon. Assuming a steel of 0·15% carbon, the upper critical point would be 900°C − 1·5 (20°C) = 870°C. About 10°C–50°C above the upper critical point is generally found suitable, and so a suitable temperature for refining would be about 900°C. The lower critical point (about 700°C) is not applicable when considering refining the core, but will be passed in order to heat the steel to above the upper critical point.

1.14 Explain the advantages of a salt bath furnace for the surface-hardening of mild steel, mentioning the type of work for which it is particularly suited.

Make a list of the safety precautions which should be observed when this type of furnace is used. (U.E.I.)

The advantages of salt bath furnaces for the surface hardening of mild steel are:
1. Rapidity of action of the carburizing when compared with pack carburizing. Overall heat-treatment time is smaller.

2. Even temperature throughout. This is especially true with the electrode salt bath where there is an automatic stirring action caused by an electromagnetic phenomenon associated with the design and the positioning of electrodes.
3. Greater hardness due to the formation of nitrides in the skin in addition to usual hardness associated with a quench-hardened high carbon steel.
4. Parts of varying shape can easily be extracted from the furnace at appropriate times.
5. Prevention of scaling of parts
   (a) in the bath, due to their being positioned beneath the salt surface
   (b) on transfer to quenching, due to the adhering salt.
6. Cleaner process due to there being no packing and unpacking of a dusty material in and out of containers.
7. The rapidity of carburizing means that the parts being carburized do not have to be held at 900°C for lengthy periods. This prevents undue grain growth and there is less chance of distortion.
8. Parts are usually quenched directly after lifting from the bath without separate refining or hardening operations.

The type of work for which the cyanide process is particularly suited is generally that of a small size required in large quantities, where the depth of case does not have to exceed about 0·5 mm, where scaling has to be avoided, where higher hardness is desirable and where grain growth has to be minimized.

Apart from the usual safety precautions (correct attitude to safe working and tidy surroundings), the following special precautions are associated with cyanide hardening:
1. The bath contains a poisonous constituent or constituents. A cupboard containing emergency antidotes must be available in the close vicinity of the furnace;
2. storage of new salt, residues and the disposal of residues, must be controlled with a high order of security;
3. the salt spatters on contact with moisture. Parts must be clean, water-free, oil-free before suspension in the bath and preferably preheated;
4. operators should wear adequate protective clothing, not only apron and gloves but also eyeshields;
5. adequate ventilation of the furnace and shop atmosphere is necessary, due to fuming.

1.15 **Describe with the aid of sketches either (i) an electric or (ii) a gas heated muffle furnace suitable for the hardening and tempering of small tools. State the usual working temperature. What precautions should be taken to avoid cracking during the heat treatment?** (U.E.I.)

Note: Since previous answers have described other types of furnace, an opportunity will be taken of describing the furnace commonly used for hardening small tools of high speed steel. Given free choice, however, the simplest furnace to describe is probably the plain furnace where the heat is provided by electrical coil elements (as Fig. 1.3a but with electric element heating). Furthermore, the temperature of such a furnace is easy to control either by the on-off operation of a thermostatic control or by continuous automatic control of the magnitude of the current. The reader is particularly requested to note the difference between temperature indication (pyrometer), temperature control (thermostat or continuous current adjustment) and continuous graphical recording (graph roll and inked, piercing, or electric pointer producing a line on the paper which unwinds at a constant rate).

A common muffle furnace used for the hardening and tempering of small cutting tools such as tool bits, milling cutters, form tools, etc., is the gas-heated two-stage muffle furnace shown diagrammatically in Fig. 1.15.

The hardening temperature of high speed steel is in the vicinity of 1350°C and in order to prevent cracking and excessive grain growth it is considered good practice to obtain this temperature in two stages: first a relatively gradual heating to about 800°C in the upper muffle, followed by a more rapid heating to about 1350°C in the lower muffle. The upper muffle can be used for the so-called tempering of high speed steel by adjusting the fuel supply so that a temperature of 300°C to 650°C is obtained. Although the heat treatment of high speed steel is often referred to as hardening and tempering, the secondary heat treatment of high speed steel leads to the acquisition of hardness rather than the sacrificing of hardness in favour of toughness. The toughness of high speed steel is obtained mainly by the quenching in air.

The main precautions to be taken to avoid cracking in any heat treatment are:
1. Avoid sharp corners and similar stress-raisers in the design of the detail;
2. carry out the heating as slowly as possible, but balance the slow

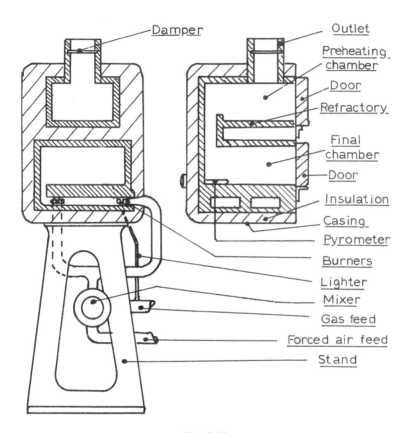

Fig. 1.15

heating against the tendency for grain growth to occur;
3. obtain the slowest rate of quenching that will provide the hardness required. The slower the quench the less danger there is of cracking. Two or more stages in the quenching may assist;
4. avoid distortion when heating (which could lead to cracking in quenching) by using supports when heating and by quenching in specific directions, dictated by the shape of the component. For example, support a long shaft in the furnace and quench vertically.

1.16   Explain fully, with the aid of sketches, the construction and the method of operation of one type of temperature-indicating equipment suitable for use with a muffle furnace.
Name a second instrument which may be used for this purpose.

If a circuit consists of two conductors of dissimilar metals, the two junctions of those metals being maintained at different temperatures, an electric current will flow in that circuit. The direction and the amount of the current depends on the materials of the conductors and the temperature difference of the junctions. For the temperatures encountered in a muffle furnace the conductors are usually of platinum and a platinum-rhodium alloy, and the hot junction is placed in the heating zone. As the current which flows is related to the temperature difference of the junctions, theoretically, for an electrical instrument to be used to indicate temperature accurately, the cold junctions should be maintained at a constant temperature.

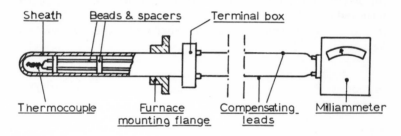

Fig. 1.16

Fig. 1.16 shows the details of a practical installation. The thermocouple of platinum and platinum-rhodium alloy wires are joined by twisting at one end, but kept from touching each other within the metallic protective sheath by silica distance pieces and beads. The thermocouple is mounted into the furnace by means of the flange and the projecting length into the furnace is arranged so that the joined end of the thermocouple is adjacent to the heating zone. The milliammeter for measuring the current is usually mounted on a convenient wall, the indicating needle recording against a scale of temperature. The compensating leads between the thermocouple and the electrical measuring instrument have an electrical effect equivalent to that of maintaining the cold junction (i.e. the terminals

of the thermocouple) at a constant temperature. The thermocouple
deteriorates in use, due to thermal strain, hence the entire outfit
should be calibrated at intervals against standard fixed points, viz:

freezing point of water	0°C
boiling point of water	100°C
boiling point of sulphur	445°C
freezing point of antimony	630°C
freezing point of silver	960°C
freezing point of gold	1060°C

A second instrument is the radiation pyrometer, which measures
temperature by focusing the rays emitted by the hot body on to a
thermocouple within the instrument itself and by converting the
thermoelectric effect to a scale reading of temperature.

**1.17/1.18(a)   Name one effect of heat, other than expansion, which is
used in an instrument for indicating heat-treatment temperatures.**
**(b) Describe the variations in this effect that occur with increasing
temperature**
**(c) Sketch, and describe, a pyrometer based on the effect of heat you
have named.** (C.G.L.I.)

An opportunity will be taken of providing alternative answers
in order to cover two types of pyrometer other than the thermocouple type described in problem 1.16.

1.17   *The Resistance Pyrometer*
(a) An effect is the variation of the resistance of a conductor of
electricity with varying temperatures.

(b) In general terms, increasing temperature causes increasing
resistance. The actual formula used is that if R_0 is the resistance at
a temperature of 0°C and R_t the resistance at a temperature of
t°C, then

$$R_t = R_0(1 + At + Bt^2 + Ct^3 + Dt^4. . .)$$

where A, B, C, D, etc. are constants.
   As a first approximation

$$R_t = R_0(1 + At) \text{ approximately}$$

and the increase in resistance is approximately proportional to the
temperature in degrees Celsius.

23

(c) A resistance pyrometer is a temperature-measuring instrument based on the effect previously described. The varying resistance is usually a platinum wire wound on thin mica plate and housed in a glazed porcelain sheath. This particular resistance assembly is fixed to the furnace so that the resistance lies in the heating zone. Leads from the resistance go to a Wheatstone bridge in the indicating instrument. This bridge is shown diagrammatically in Fig. 1.17.

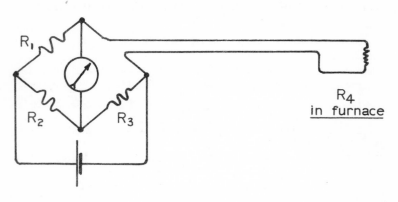

Fig. 1.17

Resistances R_1, R_2, and R_3 remain at a constant temperature.

The resistance R_4 is in the sheath in the furnace. As the temperature of R_4 varies, so does its resistance and so does the current passing through the milliammeter. By using a suitable scale and calibrating the instrument against known fixed points the milliammeter can be arranged to read furnace temperatures direct.

Alternative answer:

1.18 *The Optical Pyrometer*

(a) An effect is the radiation of light from a hot body. The wavelength of the radiation emitted varies with temperature, hence the colour of a hot body depends on temperature.

(b) If a body is in a container, no light from an outside source falls on that body, and it is said to be in 'black body' conditions. The light emanation from a hot 'black body' depends upon temperature. An article in a heat-treatment furnace approaches 'black body' conditions, and the colour of that body varies according to the following table.

Very dark red	about	600°C
Cherry red	about	900°C
Orange red	about	1000°C
Yellow	about	1100°C
Yellow-white	about	1300°C
White	about	1400°C

(c) A pyrometer based on this effect is the optical (or disappearing filament) pyrometer shown in Fig. 1.18. The radiation from the

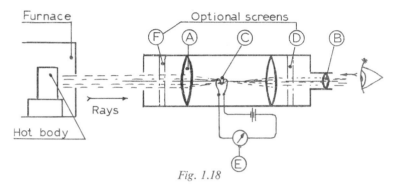

Fig. 1.18

hot body in the furnace enters lens A and is viewed through the eyepiece B. The colour of the hot body is compared with the colour of the filament C. (A suitable coloured screen can be optionally inserted at D to assist the colour match and an optional screen at F cuts out some of the damaging radiation without affecting the colour.) This filament, being within the instrument, is also in 'black body' conditions. The controlling resistance E varies the temperature of the filament. The position of the controller can be arranged to read temperature directly. If the reading is too low, the filament appears to be darker than that of the body in the furnace. If the reading is too high, the filament appears lighter. If the temperature reading is correct, the colour of the filament is the same as that of the body in the furnace, and the resulting optical illusion leads to the instrument being colloquially known as the disappearing filament pyrometer.

1.19(a) What is meant by the term 'hardness'?
(b) Describe a method of testing the hardness of a metal by mechanical means.

(c) What are the advantages and disadvantages of the method described? (U.E.I.)

(a) In a loose sense, hardness may refer to the capacity of a metal to resist abrasion, wear and cutting or deformation, either singly or any combination of two or more. It may be a condition of a whole mass (quench-hardening), of a surface (case-hardening), the effect of severe cold deformation (work-hardening), or the improvement of physical properties with time (age-hardening). In a numerical sense, and in the special context of engineering, hardness is usually determined by a consideration of the resistance offered by a material to plastic deformation caused by a loaded indenter.

(b) In the Brinell test, a steel ball of diameter d, whose hardness is not less than HV 850, is pressed into the metal by a steadily applied load of F kgf. The values of F and d, and the time that the load of F is constantly maintained depends upon the material. With steel, the ratio F/d^2 is 30 (3000 kgf with 10 mm ball or 30 kgf with 1 mm ball) and the time 15 to 30 seconds. With brass, F/d^2 is 5 and the time 60 seconds.

The Brinell hardness number (HB number) is obtained from the formula

$$\text{HB} = \frac{\text{load in kgf}}{\text{surface area of impression in mm}^2}$$

The surface area is not actually calculated. The diameter of the impression is measured on two diameters at right angles to each other with the aid of an instrument whose error should not exceed 0·02 mm. The average diameter is then obtained, and from reference to a chart the Brinell hardness number is determined, e.g. $d = 10$ mm, $F = 3000$ kgf, average diameter 4 mm, HB = 228.

(c) *Advantages*
1. a standard tensile testing machine can be used;
2. the additional equipment to carry out HB tests on a standard tensile testing machine is extremely cheap.

Disadvantages
1. Limited to metals with HB less than 450 (values obtained from the use of a carbide ball for HB numbers over 450 are considered to be 'modified' Brinell numbers);
2. difficulty of measuring diameter. The ball distorts, and impression is not a true spherical cap;

3. impression not clearly defined due to recovery of material and piling at perimeter of impression;
4. material must be thick enough to ensure no contributing effect from the support and/or backing;
5. relatively slow in operation and needs skill to provide reliable results;
6. surface to be tested has to be carefully prepared.

1.20(a) Describe a hardness test suitable for the rapid continuous assessment of the hardness of heat treated details.
(b) Name two other hardness tests.
(c) Give three reasons why you have selected the particular test in your answer to (a) rather than one of those in your answer to (b).

(a) The Rockwell hardness test obtains a hardness number from a consideration of the effect of a loaded penetrator. There are several Rockwell tests (lettered A to K inclusive except for I) for specific combinations of applied load and shape of indenter, which is either a hard steel ball or a diamond cone with a rounded tip, known as a Brale penetrator. This latter penetrator has a 120° cone angle and a rounded tip of radius 0·2 mm. A typical test for heat treated steels is the Rockwell C test using a major load of 150 kgf and the Brale penetrator.

A preliminary load of 10 kgf is applied and an indicating device set to zero. A major load of 150 kgf is then applied progressively for a few seconds and, when equilibrium has been reached, the additional load is removed but the preliminary load maintained.

The HR number is given by

$$HR = 100 - x,$$

where x is the increase in the depth of penetration due to the additional load, in units of 0·002 mm.

The actual value is not computed, it is read directly from an indicating device on the machine and, if the C test is used, a result such as HRC 63 is obtained. The test is carried out on smooth but not necessarily highly finished surfaces.

(b) Two other hardness tests are:
1. the Brinell hardness test, which provides numbers such as HB 400;
2. the Vickers hardness test, sometimes called the Diamond

Pyramid test, giving numbers such as HV 700.

(c) The Rockwell hardness test will be compared with the Vickers test.

Three advantages of the Rockwell test over the Vickers test for rapid continuous assessment are:

1. the result is more quickly obtained by the direct reading of a dial, instead of the determination of a mean diagonal from two measurements and the subsequent comparison with a chart;
2. the restriction of the Vickers test to the use of one indenter only, that of a diamond point with the angle between opposing triangular faces being 136°C;
3. the lack of the necessity for accurate determination of the shape of the impression, together with the construction of the machine ensuring the correct application of the loadings, means that less skill is required in the determination.

1.21(a) What is usually understood by toughness, as applied to the heat treatment of plain carbon steels?
(b) How is such toughness obtained after quench-hardening?
(c) Discuss briefly the information that mechanical testing can provide regarding the toughness of a heat-treated plain carbon steel.

(a) Toughness, unlike tensile strength, yield strength, etc., is a term difficult to define with exactitude. It is generally understood to be the ability of a material to withstand a suddenly applied load and thus to absorb a certain amount of energy without failure. Toughness has some relation to a combination of strength and ductility. When applied to the heat treatment of plain carbon steels, toughness is usually associated with the tempering heat treatment carried out after quench-hardening, or with the condition of the core of a case-hardened material.

(b) The toughness is acquired by tempering, which is a heat-treatment process whereby the steel is heated to a temperature below the transformation range and then cooled. The temperature is in the range of 200°C to 400°C. The treatment breaks down some of the martensite to a less brittle form and extra toughness is acquired at the expense of some of the hardness. Higher temperatures within the range quoted lead to greater toughness.

(c) The association of toughness with resistance to a suddenly applied load, such as a blow, has often led to a somewhat inaccurate assumption that an impact test of the Izod or Charpy type is a test of toughness. While these tests give a numerical value of the energy required to fracture a specimen, it must be noted very carefully that the specimen has a notch of particular form. Modern opinion tends to favour the use of Izod and Charpy tests to give some appreciation of notch sensitivity only, i.e. how a particular material behaves when given a relatively slow impact in the vicinity of a stress-raiser. The shape of the notch has a considerable effect on the results. The use of Izod and Charpy tests to assess toughness is now considered to be suspect. The greater body of authoritative opinion now leans towards using the area under the load-extension diagram, up to fracture, of the routine tensile test, as being a more reliable basis from which to obtain an indication of toughness. This area, when multiplied by the area scale, gives the work done (i.e. the energy absorbed) before fracture. Critics of this view point out, quite correctly, that the load is steadily and not suddenly applied. A reasonable conclusion is that it is probable that only when an acceptable definition of toughness, related to a numerical value, is agreed, will a suitable standard test be evolved.

CHAPTER 2

Primary Forming Processes

The questions in this chapter are based mainly upon the following items of the T2 syllabus for Mechanical Engineering Technicians:

An outline of foundry processes; the special characteristics of cast metals.

An outline of forging processes; the respective merits and uses of castings and forgings for components.

2.1(a) Make a labelled sketch of a section through the prepared mould (ready for pouring) for making a cast iron pipe 80 mm outside diameter, 40 mm internal diameter, 200 mm long with a circular flange at one end.

(b) Describe the preparation of the mould. (N.C.T.E.C.)

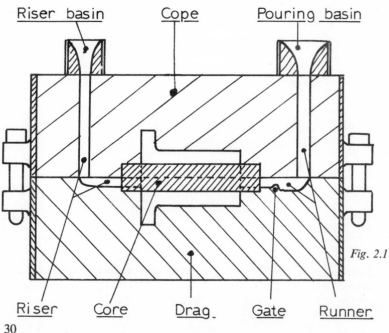

Fig. 2.1

(a) The sketch of the prepared mould is shown in Fig. 2.1.

(b) The question implies a single casting, and hence the casting would be produced by floor moulding using a 'drag and cope' mould and wooden pattern equipment. The pattern and core box would be split on the horizontal centre line.

      Sequence of mould preparation:

1. Level foundry floor, place moulding board on floor.
2. Commence to make drag, inverted position from that in Fig. 2.1.
3. Place drag box on board.
4. Place half-pattern with locating holes flat side to board, roughly central in drag.
5. Cover pattern with facing sand.
6. Fill up drag with coarse sand.
7. Ram to compact sand, strike off surplus, level with top of drag.
8. Blow off any sand on pattern face, locate second half of pattern.
9. Locate cope moulding box on drag. Sprinkle parting sand on parting face.
10. Cover pattern with facing sand, fill up cope with coarse sand, ram to compact, strike off surplus.
11. Separate the drag and cope, invert cope, rap patterns and withdraw.
12. Cut pourer and riser channels in mould with tube, enlarge at top surface of cope.
13. Prepare pourer and riser basins (pipe and sand).
14. Cut runner and gate with trowel, cut outlet to riser.
15. Dress cavity if necessary. Vent cope and drag by prodding with wire.
16. Place core in position (for core preparation see below).
17. Blow out loose sand from cavity with bellows.
18. Replace cope, place feeder and riser basins in position, move assembled mould from board to pouring station on foundry floor.

Core

Using core box, and length of wire to reinforce, compact mixture of sand and binder in core box. Split box, remove core and bake in stove. Dress core.

2.2(a) Explain briefly what is meant by plate moulding, using sketches to show:

    (i)   the plate in relation to the mould;

(ii)   the way in which several castings can be made at one pouring.
(b) Give two important advantages and two disadvantages of this method of moulding.   (C.G.L.I.)

(a) For conventional low-quantity 'floor moulding', patterns are usually constructed of wood and are split on an appropriate horizontal parting-line. The two portions of the pattern are located together with dowels. For plate moulding without the aid of a moulding machine, the pattern equipment consists of a flat plate with portions of the pattern permanently assembled, in alignment, on each side. For very large quantity production, and for very heavy castings, two plates may occasionally be used—one to assist in the making of copes, the other for drags. The plate incorporates some locating arrangement for the moulding boxes, which could be pegs in the plate, but more usually consists of holes for locating pegs. The use of a plate normally calls for moulding boxes which incorporate lugs having holes for location. Fig. 2.2 shows a typical double-sided plate used for hand or machine moulding, and shows how provision is made for several castings from one pouring.

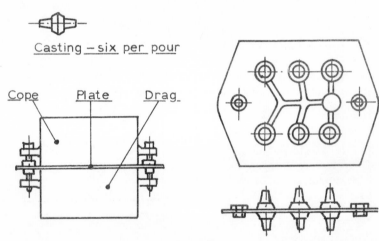

Casting – six per pour

Cope   Plate   Drag

Fig. 2.2

(b) Two important advantages are:
1. The plate includes runners, gates, part of pourer and part of riser, thus reducing considerably the time to finish the mould after the extraction of the pattern equipment. Furthermore, once the correct shape of runners and gates have been proved,

they are repeated thereafter and are no longer left to the discretion of the moulder.
2. The pattern equipment is of metal instead of wood, giving long life.

Two important disadvantages are:
1. The relatively high cost of the pattern equipment which has to be justified by large quantity production.
2. The use of a particular plate is restricted to a certain range of moulding boxes. This calls for careful planning on the use of boxes. It could lead to the carrying expense of too great a number of idle boxes.

2.3   The component shown in Fig. 2.3a is to be produced by sand casting. Outline in some detail, the essential stages employed at the foundry, if 200 castings are to be produced per week.   (W.J.E.C.)

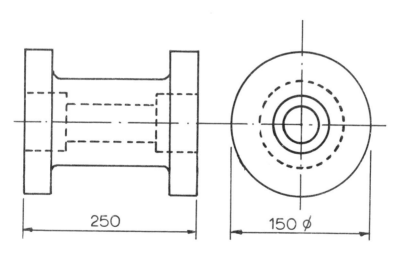

Fig. 2.3a

The continuing demand of 200 per week of a casting of an appreciable weight suggests that the work should be undertaken in a mechanized foundry possessing roller tracks or conveyors. Wooden patterns and core boxes would wear rapidly and metallic pattern equipment would be used. One pattern plate, shown in Fig. 2.3b, could be used, producing drags and copes from one

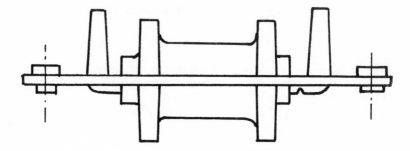

Fig. 2.3b

moulding machine. Alternatively, two moulding machines could be used, one producing copes, the other producing drags. This method would probably be more likely, due to the effort required to move complete moulds. In which case, the one plate pattern could include runners, gates, pourers and risers.

Starting at the moulding machine (or machines), the pattern plate would be placed on the machine table and a box would be located. Sand would be fed in by a sand-slinging machine and extra compacting of the sand accomplished by jolting and/or pressing. The moulds would be lifted off the plate, turned over, cleaned by an air blast and delivered to the conveyor automatically.

Cores would be made separately in a core shop—in a metallic core box using either a core-blowing machine and subsequent baking and dressing or the CO_2 process. They would be stacked near the conveyor and, as the copes and drags proceed along the conveyor, an operative or operatives would be engaged in making (or completing) risers, pourers, runners and gates, inserting the core and assembling copes and drags ready for pouring.

The completed moulds proceed to the pouring position where a continuous melting furnace would provide the molten metal. At a suitable point further along the moving conveyor track, the moulds containing hot (but now solid) castings would be pushed on to a grill and vibrated apart. Loose sand would fall through the grill to be reconditioned and passed to the sand-slinger for further use. The moulding boxes pass along a separate conveyor to be stored near the moulding machines. If necessary, the hot castings may proceed via a separate conveyor to a cooling tower. When they are at a convenient temperature, pourer and riser surplus would be knocked off, and the castings cleaned by sandblasting or shotblasting. The final operation would be the completion of the fettling

by grinding away any remaining surplus material and any unduly
rough surfaces.

2.4   Choose any simple, typical component and, using sketches,
(a) explain the purpose of using a core in the moulding process
(b) describe the method of making the core
(c) name the materials used for making the core.   (C.G.L.I.)

(a) A casting is produced by pouring molten metal into a cavity and
then allowing the metal to solidify and cool. The cavity, when cast
iron is the material, is usually formed in sand by compacting sand
around a pattern. The pattern has to be extracted from the mould
and consequently the pattern itself is a split solid. If holes or re-
entrant forms are required on the casting, separate masses of compacted sand have to be made and located in the mould cavity. These
separate masses of sand are called cores.

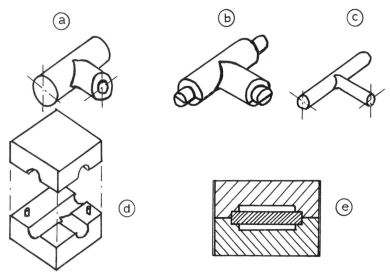

Fig. 2.4

Fig. 2.4a shows a tee-piece which has to be cast. Fig. 2.4b
shows the split pattern used in making the mould. The core prints
shown make seatings in the mould to locate the core shown in Fig.

35

2.4c, which is made in the core box shown in Fig. 2.4d. A core in a mould is shown in Fig. 2.4e.

(b) The core is made by compacting a sand-mix in the core box. Originally the core box is open and the mix is loosely compacted in each portion. Strengthening wires may be placed along the axes of the tee portions. Loose sand-mix is carefully removed from the jointing faces of the core box which is then assembled and the sand-mix is compacted by ramming from the three openings. Surplus sand is struck off each end. The core box is then opened. The 'green' core is then removed and vented with wire, baked and 'dressed'. Dressing is covering the baked core with a compound which resists the scouring action of flowing molten metal and assists the formation of a smooth surface on the casting.

(c) The main material of the core is a refractory, either a natural or a synthetic sand. The sand-mix used for core making consists of the sand together with a binder which is used to give strength after baking. A natural binder (sometimes called core-gum) is linseed oil. A synthetic binder is a synthetic resin. A recent development is to use a silicate and obtain the necessary hardness by 'gassing' with carbon dioxide, thus eliminating the baking process.

2.5(a) What is the purpose of a core when used in sandcasting?
(b) List four important characteristics of a good core sand-mix.
(c) Describe briefly what is meant by: (i) binder; (ii) blowing; (iii) baking; (iv) dressing; (v) chaplet; as applied to coremaking.

(a) A core is a shaped piece of sand-mix placed in a mould in such a way that it will be encased or partly surrounded by molten metal, and when removed from the solidified casting will leave a hole, recess or re-entrant form.

(b) A good core sand-mix should possess the following characteristics:
1. adequate dry strength and hardness after baking, or other appropriate finishing treatment;
2. sufficient 'green strength' before the finishing treatment;
3. collapsibility after casting so that the core can be easily removed;
4. refractoriness, so that a good finish will appear on or in the casting and the core will not be scoured away by the flow of molten metal.

(c) (i) A core binder is an agent added to sand to produce a good 'green' bond and also hardness after baking. A typical natural binder is linseed oil, a typical synthetic binder is a resin of the thermosetting type.

(ii) Core-blowing is a method of producing large quantities of cores by blowing a sand-mix into metal core boxes with compressed air. Even a complex core is produced in a few seconds.

(iii) Core-baking is the heating process which converts a 'green' core into a harder and more durable mass.

(iv) Core-dressing is the operation of applying a compound to the surface of a core, either in the 'green' state or after baking, for the purpose of providing protection against the scouring action of flowing molten metal and to assist the formation of a smooth surface in a cored hole or cored form.

(v) A core chaplet is a metal distance piece inserted in a mould either to prevent a core shifting its position or to give extra support to a core. The molten metal melts the chaplet which then forms part of the cast material.

2.6   Describe the process of chilling a sandcasting. Give reasons for the application of this process and compare the structure obtained with that associated with a slowly-cooled cast iron. (U.E.I.)

The carbon in a typical grey cast iron casting is mainly in the uncombined form, and appears as graphite. A grey cast iron casting is cooled slowly, the material being relatively soft and easily machineable. If a cast iron is cooled very quickly the carbon is mainly combined with the iron. Instead of the characteristic grey coloured appearance of a fracture of a grey cast iron, the appearance of a fracture of a rapidly cooled cast iron is white, the material then being referred to as white cast iron. White cast iron is intensely hard, being virtually unmachineable by conventional cutting methods.

If a casting in cast iron has to have certain parts easily machineable and other parts highly resistant to wear the requirements call for grey and white cast irons respectively. These can be obtained from the same melt by different rates of cooling. If one surface of a mould consists of metal, or there is metal very close to that surface, heat is conducted away from the molten iron very rapidly. The rapid heat conduction is called chilling—the metal used in the mould for the conduction of heat being known as chills.

The chilling produces white cast iron adjacent to the chills, with the resulting hard abrasion and wear-resistant surface. The remaining parts of the casting, being cooled more slowly in the sand mould, are of the softer and machineable grey iron.

The carbon in a slowly cooled cast iron (a grey cast iron) is mainly uncombined, appearing as flakes of free graphite with ferrite. With the rapidly cooled iron (a white cast iron) the structure includes little if any free graphite, and is mainly a mixture of iron-carbide and ferrite.

The description of chilling thus far refers to the occasions when a chill forms part of the side of the mould cavity. A chill can also be placed in a mould adjacent to a cavity and be completely surrounded by sand. In this case the chill accelerates the rate of cooling in the vicinity of the chill, and can be used to permit a portion of the casting to cool before another. When properly positioned such chills are used mainly to minimize internal strains rather than to promote a hard surface.

2.7(a) Describe briefly the difference between a sandcasting and a diecasting.
(b) Name two materials which are usually cast in sand, and two which are usually diecast.
(c) What is meant by an 'oddside' (sometimes called a 'false cope') and why is it sometimes used when sandcasting?
(d) What is meant by a 'gate' as used in sandcasting, and why are the dimensions of the gate important?

(a) A sandcasting is obtained from a mould constructed from sand. The mould is intentionally destroyed to obtain the casting. Each new casting requires a new mould.

A diecasting is obtained from a permanent metal mould. The diecasting is obtained by opening the die, which, after closing, is then ready for the next diecasting.

(b) Grey cast iron and bronze are usually cast in sand, and although high-duty aluminium alloys and zinc-base alloys can also be cast in sand, it is more usual for them to be diecast. (While most metals which can be diecast can also be sandcast, the reverse is not always true as the high pouring temperatures may damage the metallic moulds.)

(c) An oddside is used when the shape of the casting does not produce a convenient flat split in the pattern, such as a cranked lever. The pattern is solid and an oddside (or false cope) is used to assist the providing of a contoured split between cope and drag, as shown in Figs 2.7a, 2.7b, and 2.7c. An oddside is often made of plaster of Paris.

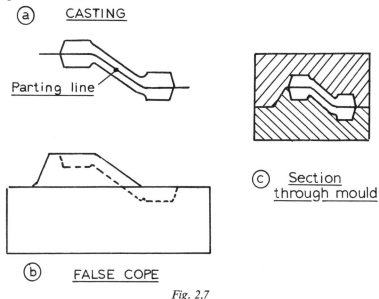

(a) CASTING

Parting line

(c) Section through mould

(b) FALSE COPE

Fig. 2.7

(**d**) A gate is positioned in the runner, close to the mould cavity, and controls the flow of molten metal into a mould cavity. The dimensions must be large enough to allow the molten metal to fill the cavity rapidly, but not so large that the stream scours away the mould cavity.

2.8   Define the following terms and state whether they apply to foundry or forging practice: (i) fettling; (ii) strickle; (iii) bloom; (iv) drag; (v) vent.   (U.L.C.I.)

(**i**)   *Fettling* is a general term used to describe the cleaning and dressing operations carried out upon castings or forgings. Although the term is strictly appropriate to both foundry and forging practice, common usage usually associates fettling with foundry practice, particularly to the removal of surplus material from a rough casting after moulding.

(ii) *Strickle* is a term used in foundry practice to describe a form of board or plate employed for shaping a mould or core. The strickle has a suitably shaped profile and is either drawn along the sand or rotated about a vertical post; it is generally used for forming the moulds of large castings of circular shape.

(iii) *Bloom* is a term used in forging practice to describe a semi-finished metal product, having a rectangular cross-section with rounded corners, that is produced by rolling or forging ingots. A bloom normally refers to a cross-sectional area of over 150 mm × 150 mm, and is usually further processed to a smaller cross-sectional area and cut off to appropriate lengths to form the billets for forging.

(iv) *Drag* is a term used in foundry practice to describe the lower portion of a split mould. The more common form of split mould usually has two parts and is referred to as a 'drag and cope' mould.

(v) *Vent* is a term used in foundry practice to describe any small opening in a completed mould which provides an escape for the gases liberated when molten metal enters the mould. Vent holes are usually made with wire of small diameter and can be produced in the mould body and/or cores.

2.9(a) Describe, briefly, three of the following terms used in foundry practice: (i) dry sand, (ii) riser, (iii) core-print, (iv) rammer, and (v) runner.
(b) A replacement bolt is required to the following specification: Shank, 20 mm diameter and 150 mm long; head, 40 mm square and 20 mm thick. Describe the process of forging the head of the bolt. The bolt is to be made from 20 mm diameter black steel bar. (U.L.C.I.)

(a) (i) Dry sand is a term used to describe a mould. A 'dry sand mould' is a mould which has been dried in an oven before the metal is poured in. It is a technique often used when an improved surface finish is required on a casting.

(ii) A riser is a reservoir connected to the casting so as to provide liquid metal to the casting during solidification. The metal in the riser will offset the shrinkage which occurs when the casting solidifies. The riser is removed from the cold casting by fettling.

(iii) A core-print is a projection on a pattern. The print makes a cavity in the mould which is used for locating a core.

Alternative answers.

(iv) A rammer is a tool used by a moulder for compacting sand in a mould. A moulder usually possesses several rammers, some being flat, others wedge-shaped, some long and narrow. He chooses the rammer according to the shape of the volume to be compacted.

(v) A runner is a channel, usually horizontal, cut in a mould, through which the molten metal flows towards, or is distributed around, the mould cavity. A runner begins at the bottom of the pouring hole and terminates at a gate, the gate controlling the flow of metal into the mould cavity.

(b) The head has a volume of $40 \times 40 \times 20 = 32\,000$ mm^3. The cross-sectional area of the shank is 314·2 mm^2, hence the extra length required is $32\,000/314\cdot2$, which is very nearly 100 mm.

The blank should be 20 mm diameter and 250 mm long. The first stage in the forging is to increase the cross-sectional area at one end. One end of the blank would be heated to forging temperature and the cross-sectional area at the hot end increased by 'upsetting'. A swage block could be placed on the anvil and, if necessary, a slug dropped in a suitable hole so that a 150 mm length of the shank is contained in the swage block. The head would be upset to about 20 mm thickness and of roughly cylindrical form by hammering in about three heatings. The next step would be to form the square with the aid of top and bottom formers having 90° vees. The work should be indexed round at intervals to bring the square head gradually to form. Forming the head should be accomplished with about three heatings. The final step would be to planish the head by heating and hammering with a 'flatter'.

The number of heatings would be decided by the smith so as to avoid grain growth on prolonged heating and to carry out the final sizing at a temperature just above the recrystallization temperature of the metal. The smith may also decide to carry out the original upsetting by 'jumping-up' the hot end on an anvil or using circular swage grips in a vice. The method of upsetting is a matter of personal preference.

2.10(a) What is the difference between a casting and a forging?
(b) State and briefly describe two types of casting methods and two types of forging methods.
(c) Name and briefly describe, giving a reason in each case, three defects which may be found in sandcastings, and three which may be found in drop-forgings.

(a) A casting is a metallic object which has been manufactured by pouring molten metal into sand, metal or other moulds and allowing the metal to solidify.

A forging is a metallic object which has been manufactured by forming into the required shape by hammering and/or pressing.

(b) 1. Sandcasting uses moulds constructed from sand. The moulds are destroyed to extract the casting.

Diecasting uses metallic moulds which are permanent. The molten metal may be fed by gravity or by pressure.

2. Drop-forging shapes the metal by means of a falling weight (to which may be attached 'top half' of the die) forcing heated metal into a die (or between dies).

Press-forging shapes the metal in a similar manner to drop-forging, i.e. using a die or dies, but the pressure is relatively slowly applied in a press instead of by the impact of a falling weight.

(c) *Casting defects*

1. A *blowhole* is a cavity in a casting formed by the evolution of dissolved gas that fails to escape when the metal solidifies. The main cause is too great a moisture content in the sand.
2. A *misrun* occurs when a section thickness is too thin, or the metal is too cold, so that the entire cavity in the mould is not filled with metal.
3. A *cold shut* occurs when two or more streams of metal meet in the mould cavity and are too cold to fuse together.

Forging defects

1. A *mismatch* occurs in drop-forging when the dies are incorrectly aligned, and results in a lateral displacement between portions of the forging.
2. *Scale pits* are shallow surface depressions caused by not removing scale from the dies. The scale is subsequently worked into the surface of the forging. ·
3. An *unfilled section* is similar to a misrun in casting, and occurs when metal does not completely fill the die cavity. It is usually caused by using insufficient metal or insufficient heating of the metal.

2.11(a) Describe four advantages of cast iron for engineering purposes giving a reason in each case why it is considered advantageous.

(b) Name and briefly describe a type of cast iron other than grey cast iron which is commonly used in engineering.

(c) State the range of temperature at which forging is carried out on a plain carbon steel and explain the reasons for the particular temperature range.

(d) What is meant by draft on a forging and why is it necessary?

(a) 1. Cast iron is cheap, both as a basic material and in its processing, and is favoured when the cost of the final product is of major importance.

2. Cast iron can be obtained in a wide range of properties—from an easily machined grey cast iron to an alloy cast iron whose properties approach that of steel. The range gives designers considerable freedom in selecting an appropriate cast iron.

3. Cast iron is extremely strong in compression, and is particularly suitable for heavy masses loaded in compression, e.g. structural bases.

4. Cast iron (particularly grey cast iron) tends to absorb vibration, and is therefore an extremely useful material for the main structures of machine tools.

(b) Malleable cast iron is obtained by intentionally casting a white cast iron and then by a subsequent lengthy heating modifying the carbon in its structure so as to produce a 'whiteheart' or 'blackheart' fracture. Malleable cast iron is not brittle and its physical properties approach those of wrought iron; it is therefore used where a casting is required which has to be subjected to shock loading.

(c) The forging range is determined by the percentage of carbon. It must be high enough to make the steel easily deformable by applied loads and to be above the recrystallization temperature to avoid work-hardening, but not so high as to cause excessive grain growth and burning.

The range 1150°C to 1300°C would be suitable for a steel of about 0·2% carbon, and a range of 1000°C to 1150°C for a steel of about 0·7% carbon.

(d) Draft is a taper on the profile of a forged component to allow the metal to flow in the closing dies and to facilitate extraction of the forging from the dies. A suitable draft angle is about 7°, as shown in Fig. 2.11.

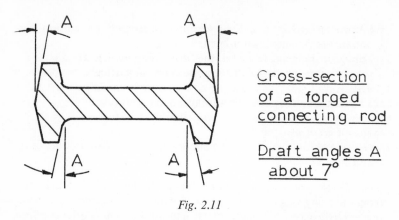

Cross-section
of a forged
connecting rod

Draft angles A
about 7°

Fig. 2.11

2.12(a) Tabulate, in order of importance, the main factors that determine whether engineering components are to be supplied as castings or forgings.
(b) (i) Why is it inadvisable for a casting to have sudden changes of section?
(ii) For what purpose are steel chills sometimes inserted in a sand mould intended for grey cast iron casting? (W.J.E.C.)

(a) It is difficult to tabulate the main factors in an all-embracing order of importance as, under special circumstances, the particular importance of what is normally a minor factor may easily outweigh what may be so-called major considerations. A firm may well prefer to accept certain deficiencies when embarking upon a proposal. For instance, although forgings may be slightly preferable, the firm may find that only castings can be obtained within a particular time schedule to meet a delivery date. Furthermore, in many cases, a material specification prevents any choice at all, e.g. if malleable iron is specified a casting naturally results.

Under normal circumstances, consideration is broadly given to the following:
1. The functional requirements of the component. Forgings in general have better physical properties such as tensile strength, fatigue-resistance and impact-resistance. However, cast iron is a better vibration absorber.
2. The overall cost, in terms of
   (*a*) first cost of equipment, e.g. patterns or dies,
   (*b*) cost of raw material, e.g. cast iron or steel,

(*c*) processing costs, e.g. machining a forging or casting to obtain the finished component.
3. The geometric shapes and the machining which results, e.g. re-entrant shapes and holes can be cored in castings.
4. The overall size, affecting the ease of supply and delivery time.
5. The accuracy required from unmachined features.
6. The structure of the component, particularly the occurrence of abrupt changes of section.
7. Operations after the final machining, such as welding, finishing and heat treatment.

(b) (i) 1. As the casting solidifies, metal should flow easily from runners and risers, otherwise cavities or misruns occur.

2. As the casting cools further while solid, it will contract. Thin sections cool more rapidly than thick sections and differing rates of contraction may cause cracks and/or internal strains.

(ii) Steel chills are mainly used when a hard surface is required on a relatively softer grey iron body. The chills rapidly cool areas in their proximity and tend to form the hard 'white cast iron' on parts of the casting in their vicinity. A secondary usage is to create more uniform cooling and hence minimize internal strains.

2.13(a) Drop-forging is a manufacturing process often used to produce components which are subject to severe stresses. Describe briefly the technique of drop-forging.
(b) State two reasons why certain components cannot be produced by the drop-forging process.   (W.J.E.C.)

(a) A drop-forging is manufactured by shaping hot plastic metal within closing dies. The single blow or a multiplicity of blows causes a metal slug or preform to flow and compact itself in the dies to the shape of the impressions. A bottom die is secured to the anvil of the machine, and remains stationary. A top die is secured to a ram and accurately aligned with the bottom die. The ram is raised and then allowed to fall freely under gravitational influence. The fall usually ranges from one to three metres. The lift can be made by a frictional device or by air pressure, control being effected by a treadle. The dies can have one impression (as with simple circular forgings) but with complicated shapes there may be several stages on one set of dies, plus a trimming operation.

In order to ensure that the material fills the cavities, a small amount of excess material occurs in the slug or preform. This material is squeezed out between the faces of the dies and is known as flash. It is usually removed in a separate pressing operation.

(b) Two reasons are (1) poor forgeability of material and (2) design of the component.

1. The material must be capable of being forged. Some materials, such as most steels, especially those with low carbon content, forge readily. A similar process occurs with a 60/40 brass, but the blow is not so severe, and is more like a 'squeezing' than a 'hitting'. However, a component in 70/30 brass should not be drop-forged. This material is 'hot short', i.e. it does not flow satisfactorily when hot.

2. The geometrical shape of the component may prevent it from being drop-forged. A conventional drop-forging rarely has holes in it, and certainly not deep holes of small diameter, while components with re-entrant forms cannot be drop-forged. Small radii (especially with fillets), sharp corners and abrupt changes of section must be avoided. Apart from design shape, size itself is a criterion. There is a limit to the size of a drop-forging due to the size of the machine. Although machines are getting larger, it is rare for a drop-forging to have a face exceeding 300 mm square.

2.14(a) Describe one of the following processes:
  (i) drop-forging
  (ii) bar rolling
  (iii) sand moulding
(b) What type of material do you associate with each process?
(c) Give a typical application where each is used and comment on the difference in the physical properties.   (Y.C.F.E.)

Note: As drop-forging and sand moulding have been covered previously, the bar rolling topic will be chosen as the answer to **(a)**.

(a) (ii) Rolling is a term used to describe the working of metal by passing it between rollers which revolve in opposite directions. The metal is compressed, reduced in section and elongated, with no real significant change in volume. The operation may be carried out hot, when the resulting product has a 'black' finish due to scale. If carried out cold, the product has a 'bright' finish. For bar rolling the rolls are grooved to provide the required shape of cross-section. The raw material is a billet whose cross-section is normally less than

150 mm × 150 mm, being square with rounded corners. The billet is itself rolled from a bloom obtained by manipulating an ingot. Reduction from the billet to the final cross-section of the bar usually requires several passes, the bar being turned through 90° at each pass to obtain uniform reduction all round. As an example, progressive reductions from a 100 mm square billet may be to oval, 75 mm square, oval, 50 mm square, oval, to 40 mm diameter. The rolling mill may be two-high (with a reversing arrangement), three-high (alternate passes top and bottom rolls), four-high with backing rolls, or clusters. In addition to the primary object of reduction of cross-section, rolling may improve grain structure, the physical properties and the surface finish.

(b) Forgings are mainly of ferrous materials, but certain aluminium alloys produce sound forgings and a similar process for brass is termed hot pressing. Forgings, due to directional properties obtained during the forging process, show improved resistance to shock loading. Ferrous materials commonly associated with drop-forging are mild steel of specification En 3b and '40 carbon steel' of specification En 8.

Bar rolling is itself a forging process, to which the remarks above are equally applicable. Typical materials are wrought steels. (Aluminium alloys and brasses in bar form are usually extruded.)

Castings can be obtained from most metallic materials, but usually have a coarse structure which gives less resistance to shock than a forging. A typical material is grey cast iron.

(c) A typical forging is a stub-axle for automotive use. A typical rolled bar is a 40 mm round bar for subsequent machining on capstan lathes. A typical casting is the bed of a lathe.

In general, a grey iron casting is strong in compression, weak in tension, brittle and relatively soft. The properties of a rolled bar depend upon the material specification and the range is immense. Substantial differences from castings are the improved properties in a lengthwise direction associated with rolling and an improved grain structure.

The properties of forgings again depend on the material specification. The range is immense but in this case as distinct from the uni-directional properties of a rolled bar, forging gives an opportunity of producing improved properties in specified directions, e.g. parallel to an eventual tooth profile in a forged gear blank.

2.15(a) Write brief notes on the following terms used in a forging process: (i) flash; (ii) top and bottom die; (iii) upset forging.
(b) Give a brief account of the relative advantages of diecastings and drop-forgings. (N.C.T.E.C.)

(a) (i) Flash is the excess material squeezed out between the faces of closing dies in a machine-forging operation, such as drop-forging and press-forging; it is removed by a clipping operation. Flash is unavoidable but kept to a minimum to ensure that sufficient material is available in the billet, slug or preform to fill the die cavities.

(ii) Top and bottom dies contain the cavities into which metal flows in a drop-forging operation. The bottom die is fixed to a table. The top die is attached to a slide which is lifted vertically and allowed to fall by the influence of gravity on to a billet, slug or preform. The metal then flows into the die cavities.

(iii) Upset forging is a hand- or machine-forging process used to increase a cross-section. A typical example is forming the head of a bolt on circular bar where the cross-section of the bar is that of the shank of the bolt.

(b) Diecastings are obtained from permanent metallic moulds and hence the accuracy of the resulting diecasting can be closely controlled. This leads to two important advantages of diecastings when compared with drop-forgings: accuracy and consistency. Accuracy in drop-forging mainly depends on the amount of flash, while consistency depends not only on flash but also on the heating.

The structures of the products are different. Castings have different structures from the outside in. Small grain size at a surface changes to a larger grain size on the interior. Provided drop-forging is undertaken so that the final temperature is just above the recrystallization temperature, the grain size is small and uniform.

In general, forgings have greater tensile strengths and are harder than castings. They are also more resistant to fatigue and shock loading due to the directional properties of a forging which are absent in a casting. Provided the cost of dies is justified, a diecasting can include holes and recesses which could eliminate, or at least reduce the cost of, subsequent machining. A diecasting will also reproduce fine surface detail (e.g. trade names) more uniformly than a forging and the surface finish is generally more uniform, has a smoother texture and is free from scale.

2.16   Give reasons for any three of the following and explain how they may be corrected or avoided.
(a) Stresses and cracks in castings
(b) Excessive grain size in a steel forging
(c) Coarse grained core in a case-hardened steel
(d) Hard and soft spots in a 'hardened' steel.   (U.E.I.)

(a) This fault usually lies in design, and is caused by contractions as the casting cools. The usual errors are abrupt changes of thickness of section, corner radii being too sharp and incorrect positioning and/or absence of webs. Even with correct design, stresses and cracks could be caused by too rapid cooling.

Stresses can be relieved by 'stress relieving' by natural weathering after a preliminary machining, or by artificial stress relieving by a suitable heat treatment. Cracks can only be avoided by correct design. A casting should be left to cool in the mould for as long as possible.

(b) Excessive grain size is caused by forging at too high a temperature. It is prevented by arranging for several heatings during the forging operation, so that the final forging is completed slightly above the recrystallization temperature. This produces a forging with small grain size.

(c) A coarse grained core is caused by prolonged heating during the carburizing process. It can be avoided by using a nickel alloy case-hardening steel instead of a plain carbon steel, or using a more active carburizing medium, such as cyanide instead of animal charcoal. If it does occur it can be corrected by a refining heat-treatment.

Additional answer (note that the question only called for answers to any three):
(d) This fault is usually caused by decarburization of the surface, the component then having a surface of variable carbon content. Steel manufacture is so precise that it is rarely due to the original material, the more probable cause is variations in furnace atmosphere during heating previous to hardening. It can be prevented by using a controlled atmosphere furnace or by heating in a neutral salt bath. Occasionally, the fault may be caused by not agitating the quenching media and allowing bubbles to adhere to the surface; this causes different rates of cooling at different portions of the surface. The fault can be varied by rapid movement of the article and/or the quenching media.

CHAPTER 3

Measurement

The questions in this chapter are based mainly upon the following items of the T2 syllabus for Mechanical Engineering Technicians:

The use of flat surfaces and reference planes; use of the level, height gauge and depth gauge; the dial indicator, its accessories and uses; slip gauges; their use as reference blocks in the workshop.
The answers, in general, relate to the construction of the equipment. Other answers relating to their uses can be found in Chapter 7—manufacturing methods.

3.1(a) State two uses of a surface plate.
(b) Describe briefly the accuracy requirements for flatness of cast iron surface plates, and how those requirements limit their use for measurements to a high order of precision.
(c) State two materials, other than cast iron, from which surface plates can be made. State four advantages which result from the use of these materials.

(a) 1. As a datum reference plane for marking out or inspection.
    2. To check the flatness of another surface.

(b) Cast iron surface plates are made in two grades of accuracy (A and B) up to about 2 metres × 1½ metres, and in grade B only, over this size, up to about 4 metres × 3 metres. Grade A surface plates have flatness tolerances which are one-quarter of those for Grade B of similar size. The tolerance on flatness is the distance which separates two imaginary planes which just enclose the surface. (A typical example of accuracy is within 0·005 mm for a 300 mm × 200 mm Grade A plate.)

    One of these planes is called the bearing surface, and is the plane containing the so-called 'high spots' of the surface plate. For Grade A plates this must contain not less than 20% of the surface area, and 10% for Grade B. The percentage of high spots must not be so high as to cause wringing of slip gauges. In addition, if the surface plates are over 600 mm × 400 mm, there is a flatness accuracy requirement of about 0·005 mm over any area of about one-tenth of a square metre.

The surface of a cast iron surface plate is produced by scraping, or a grinding process which furnishes a similar type of surface to that obtained by scraping. A primary requirement is that the finish must not be of sufficient degree that causes slip gauges to wring to the surface. Very precise determinations usually require the use of slip gauges, a method which loses its accuracy if wringing is not obtained. Furthermore, the gauging surface of a slip gauge has a relatively small area compared with the plate, and it may contact the surface plate in a particular area which is relatively inaccurate in itself, but the area could still be within the tolerance for the whole surface of the plate.

(c) Surface plates can also be made of non-metallic substances such as granite and glass.

Four advantages, in comparison with cast iron surface plates are:

1. Granite and glass plates of similar depth are more rigid than cast iron plates.
2. Damage to their surfaces causes indentation and does not throw up a projecting burr.
3. Corrosion is virtually absent.
4. It is easier to slide metallic articles, such as height gauges and squares, on their surfaces.

3.2(a) Write a short account of the importance of reference planes in engineering measurement and manufacture.
(b) Describe a suitable method of measuring the angle on a morse taper shank.   (W.J.E.C.)

(a) If we add to the x and y axes of ordinary graphical co-ordinates a third z axis which passes through the origin, at right-angles to both the x axis and the y axis, three basic reference axes can be obtained. The plane containing the 'xy' axes is usually considered to be horizontal, and those containing the 'xz' and 'yz' axes are then two vertical planes.

The position of ANY point, line or plane can be precisely stated with reference to the three basic planes and consequently the

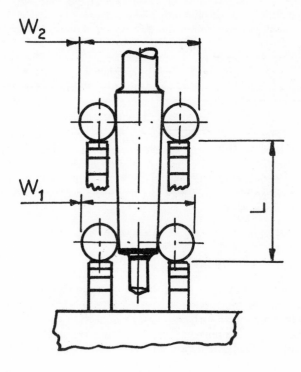

Fig. 3.2

co-ordinate planes are used as reference planes for engineering measurement and manufacture.

Translating the foregoing theoretical principles to the workshop environment, a practical example in measurement is the use of a surface plate and an angle block. If a detail to be measured is secured to the angle block, measurements can be taken from the reference planes and, by appropriate arithmetic, the dimensional relationships of the detail can be established. A practical example in manufacturing would be to use the table of a machine tool as the horizontal plane, with table edges as vertical reference planes.

It should be borne in mind when dimensioning and machining engineering details that the selection of reference planes must be made with due consideration to the functional requirements of the detail. The largest and/or most convenient flat surface is not necessarily the ideal plane to use as a datum.

(b) *Note: If the morse taper is part of a tool which is centred at each end, or suitable attachments are available, the best way is to use sine centres, as used in the solution to problem 3.18.*

The method in the answer which follows presumes no centres or attachments exist.

The taper is usually set vertically and rollers of equal diameter rest on suitable slip gauge piles as shown in Fig. 3.2. From the heights of the slip gauge piles the value of the dimension L can be determined. Values of W_2 and W_1 are obtained from a vernier calliper, micrometer or a floating carriage machine, depending upon the accuracy desired.

$$\text{Included angle} = 2\left(\tan^{-1}\frac{W_2 - W_1}{2L}\right)$$

3.3(a) Explain the meaning of the term 'cross-wind' in relation to cast iron surface plates.
(b) Describe a suitable method for testing the surface of a cast iron surface plate to detect cross-wind. (C.G.L.I.)

(a) Cross-wind is a deviation from flatness, somewhat similar to twisting. Fig. 3.3a shows a cross-wound surface plate, with imaginary lines drawn on the surface. Suppose the height of every intersection was known from a suitable datum. Consider vertical sections through lines 1–1 and lines 4–4 with points A1 and A4 superimposed, as shown in Fig. 3.3b. Line F_1F_4 is at an angle to line A_1A_4, and illustrates cross-wind, i.e. an effect similar to holding one edge and twisting the opposing edge.

(b) Cross-wind can be detected by mapping the contour of the plate by using a level of length AB ($=1–2$) as shown in Fig. 3.3a (alternatively, a travelling dial indicator could be used). Starting at point A1, the level is moved at stages along line 1–1. The difference in height of the two ends of the level at each stage is noted. The level is then moved successively along lines 2–2, 3–3 and 4–4, then finally along lines AA and FF.

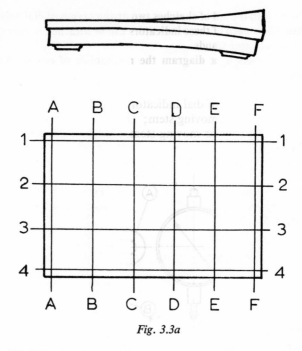

Fig. 3.3a

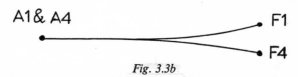

Fig. 3.3b

A chart can now be drawn up of the nominal vertical height of each intersection. As a first approach, points A1 and A4 can be brought to a basic level, by adding or subtracting a constant amount to all points on line 4–4. Points A1 and A4 are now at the same level. Cross-wind may quickly be revealed by a difference in the values of the heights of F1 and F4. If these are at the same height, it should not be assumed that cross-wind is absent. The heights along lines 2–2 and 3–3 should now be proportionally adjusted and then values compared along lines BB, CC, DD, etc. A plate could quite easily be true for a portion of its surface, with cross-wind confined to a particular area.

**3.4(a) Show with the aid of sketches two distinct types of dial indicator.
(b) Describe how each of these indicators can be attached to accessories
such as dial indicator stands.**
**(c) Show by means of a diagram the mechanism of one of the dial
indicators.**

(a) Two distinct types of dial indicator are:
1. those with a linear moving stem;
2. those with an angular moving stem, shown diagrammatically in
    Fig. 3.4a.

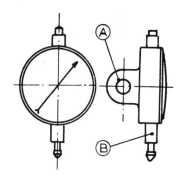

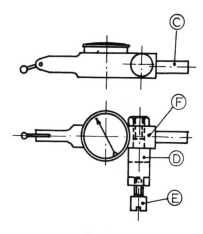

Fig. 3.4a

(b) The more common form of dial indicator, shown on the left in Fig. 3.4a is usually attached by a holding screw through the hole marked A. In certain cases, the indicator can be held by a clamp around the diameter B, but care must be taken to avoid undue pressure to allow free movement of the plunger.

With the lever type shown on the right in Fig. 3.4a, the attachment depends upon the design. Depending upon the design, a clamp may be attached on the circular portion marked C, a rod may be passed through the hole in the extension piece D, then clamped with screw E or a clamp may be used over the rectangular section marked F (with the extension piece removed).

(c) The mechanism of a typical conventional dial indicator is shown in Fig. 3.4b. The rack on the plunger turns compound wheel A.

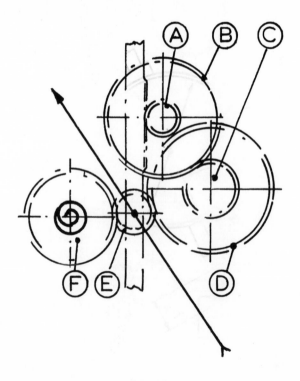

Fig. 3.4b

Teeth B drive compound wheel C. Teeth D drive final wheel E, to which the pointer is attached. The final wheel E provides a drive to a wheel F to which a coil spring is attached to provide measuring pressure and pointer return.

3.5(a) Explain the error that can occur in the reading of a dial indicator if the spindle is not square to the surface being checked for height. Calculate the error, correct to four decimal places, in the dial reading when the angle of the spindle is 20° to the vertical and the true difference in height is 0·06 mm. Take cosine 20° = 0·940 0.
(b) List the slips to be wrung together to produce an overall dimension of 68·931 mm. Your set must include two protection slips. (U.L.C.I.)

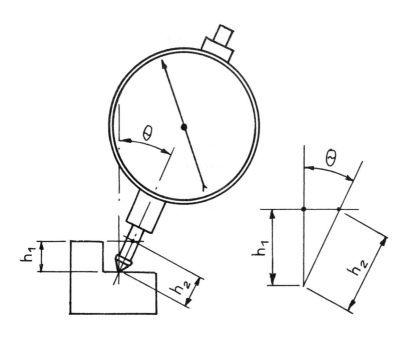

Fig. 3.5

(a) Fig. 3.5 shows a dial indicator set at an angle θ to the true direction of a difference in levels of h_1. The dial indicator stem moves a distance of h_2, and indicates on its dial a difference of h_2 instead of the true difference of h_1.

Now $$\frac{h_1}{h_2} = \cos\theta, \quad \text{and} \quad h_2 = \frac{h_1}{\cos\theta}$$

Amount of error = indicated reading – correct dimension
$$= h_2 - h_1$$
$$= \frac{h_1}{\cos\theta} - h_1$$

For the given circumstance, $h_1 = 0{\cdot}06$ mm and $\cos\theta = 0{\cdot}94$.

Hence $$\text{error} = 0{\cdot}06\left(\frac{1}{0{\cdot}94} - 1\right)$$

By ordinary division

$$\frac{1}{0{\cdot}94} = 1{\cdot}053\,2$$

Error $= 0{\cdot}06$ mm $(1{\cdot}053\,2 - 1)$
$= 0{\cdot}06$ mm $(0{\cdot}053\,2)$
$= 0{\cdot}003\,192$
$= 0{\cdot}003\,2$ mm to four decimal places, and the reading is greater than the true dimension.

(b)

Original dimension =	68·931
Less two protector slips of 2·5 mm =	5
	63·931
1 mm + 3rd place	1·001
	62·93
1 mm + 2nd place	1·03
	61·90
1 mm + 1st place	1·9
	60·0
To bring whole number 25, 50 or 75	10
	50

Combination

$= 2$ protector slips of 2·5 mm

plus 1·001, 1·03, 1·9, 10 and 50 mm.

3.6 **Explain, with the aid of diagrams, a typical application of the dial indicator for setting-up purposes on:**
(a) the milling machine
(b) the drilling machine.

In each case show and/or state clearly: (i) the object of the test; (ii) the attachments required; (iii) the method of mounting the indicator; (iv) the motions to be used. (C.G.L.I.)

(a) Milling machine

(i) Object: to line up a casting (such as an angle plate) so that a machined vertical face is in line with the tenon slot.

(ii) Attachments: test indicator set (base having push pins), with vertical pillar, universal joint, cross rod.

(iii) Mounting: see Fig. 3.6a. Dial indicator clamped to cross rod with knurled nut.

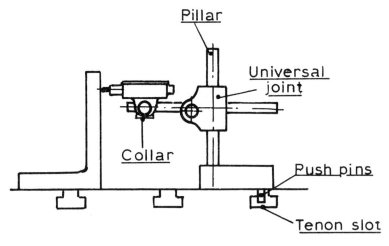

Fig. 3.6a

(iv) Motion: dial indicator set is traversed along tenon slot by hand with push pins contacting one side of the tenon slot.

59

(b) Drilling machine

(i)   Object: to line up a machined surface on an irregular casting, square with the spindle, on a single spindle drilling machine.

(ii)   Attachments: morse taper holder, cross bar. Dial indicator fixed to cross bar with knurled screw.

(iii)   Mounting: see Fig. 3.6b.

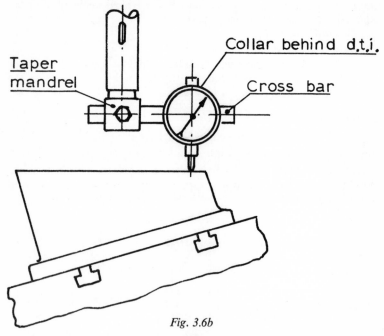

Fig. 3.6b

(iv)   Motion: drive to spindle thrown out of gear. Spindle lowered till indicator reading obtained. Spindle rotated by inching or by hand.

3.7   A batch of 500 headed pins is to be made to the dimensions shown in Fig. 3.7a.

(a) Using sketches, explain how a dial gauge can be set up and used as a comparator to measure the 10 mm thickness of the head.

(b) What type of dial gauge would be suitable for this purpose, what graduations should it have, and what would be the accuracy of the measurement available?

(C.G.L.I.)

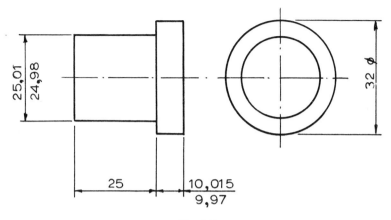

Fig. 3.7a

(a) The tolerance of 0·045 mm is so small that special precautions are necessary to obtain a sufficient degree of accuracy. The dial gauge should be used in conjunction with a comparator stand, as shown in Fig. 3.7b. The important feature, apart from the general rigidity of

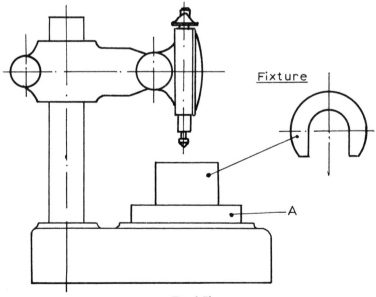

Fig. 3.7b

the set-up, is the precision lapped table surface A (a scraped cast iron reference plane will not provide a sufficient degree of accuracy). A fixture B will be required, based on a hardened plain bush of outside diameter 40 mm, inside diameter 26 mm and length 30 mm, cutaway to assist loading and unloading, and the ends being of a precision lapped finish. A 10 mm slip gauge would be wrung on the bush. The dial gauge would be lowered until a reading is obtained, the cover dial rotated until the needle is opposite the zero mark, and 'go' and 'not-go' indicators placed at the + 15 and − 30 markings. Checking is undertaken by raising the dial indicator stem, placing a component in the bush, placing the assembly on the table, lowering the stem carefully on to the head and gently moving the bush and component around under the stem. Correct work is indicated by the pointer remaining within the 'go' and 'not-go' pointers.

(b) The dial indicator should be of high quality and of conventional design, except that a lever is fitted to raise and lower the plunger. As a general rule, it is convenient to use a dial whose full travel is twice the tolerance, in this case about 0·090 mm. The nearest standard would be 0·1 mm and graduated 50–0–50, each graduation therefore is equivalent to 0·001 mm.

An estimation of the accuracy of the measurement that would be available is difficult to state precisely.

In general, errors of determination are due to:
1. errors in the equipment,
2. errors in the setting,
3. errors in the use,

and some of these can be mutually cancelling.

In this particular case, it will be presumed that the setting would be checked at regular intervals against the 10 mm gauge block, in which case errors in the equipment and the setting are a minor consideration. The greatest error that would probably arise would be in the use, particularly with careless inspection. Presuming a skilled person handles the equipment, the accuracy should be within two divisions on the dial indicator, i.e. within 0·002 mm of true size. As a general guide, equipment, setting and methods should be chosen so that a determination is more accurate than one-tenth of the tolerance.

3.8(a) Describe with the aid of sketches the method of wringing slip gauges together.
(b) Why are two 2·5 mm slip gauges provided in a set of gauges?

(c) Write brief notes on the care and use of slip gauges.
(d) Make up a combination of slip gauges of 74·17 mm.   (U.E.I.)

(a) Slip gauges should be 'wrung' together in such a manner that any moisture, oil, dust or similar foreign matter will be pushed away from the gauging surfaces instead of being trapped between the gauges. Fig. 3.8 shows the usual method.

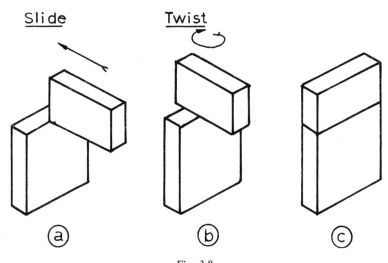

Fig. 3.8

(b) Two 2·5 mm slip gauges are usually included in a typical metric set of workshop or inspection grade for use in a combination to act as 'protectors' by concentrating wear on two gauges, hence minimizing wear on others. In addition it is cheaper to replace these protectors than the larger sizes. Protector slips are not normally *supplied* with calibration and reference sets but users of these sets often prefer to purchase protectors as a separate item.

(c) The following points are considered good practice in the care and use of slip gauges:

Care
1. Store gauges not in use in the box.
2. Keep box closed.
3. Avoid contacting gauging surfaces with fingers.

4. Avoid storage in an atmosphere which is humid or where dust is prevalent.
5. Check accuracy at appropriate intervals.

Use
1. Keep storage box closed as much as possible.
2. Wipe gauging surfaces before and after use with a sulphur-free, lint-free cloth bearing a solvent such as trichlorethylene.
3. Wring together in a correct manner.
4. Use 2·5 mm protector slips when possible.
5. Check sizes as used by inspecting the marking on the slip gauges and not relying on vacant positions in the box.
6. Use minimum number of gauges for a combination.
7. Do not leave wrung together for long periods.

(d)

	74·17
2 protectors at 2·5 mm	5
	69·17
1 + second place	1·07
	68·1
1 + first place	1·1
	67·0
Excess of 50	17·0
Final size	50·0

Pile consists of two 2·5 mm protectors, plus 1·07, 1·1, 17 and 50 mm slip gauges

Note: There are differences of opinion on the cause of the wringing action between slip gauges. Some operators find that a minute film of lubricant and/or moisture assists their own particular wringing action. Too much lubricant may tend to attract foreign particles, and moisture provided by the breath is acid, causing corrosion. The greatest body of opinion feels that the wringing action is due to molecular attraction and that it is good practice to have the slip gauge surfaces chemically and mechanically clean.

3.9(a) List the gauges that are found in a set of metric slip gauges which enables increments of 0·001 mm to be obtained.
(b) Obtain the sizes of the gauges that would make up a pile of 49·517

mm, the combination to include two protector slips.
(c) **What is meant by the length of a slip gauge, and why is this particular definition used?**
(d) **List, and indicate the use of, the four grades of accuracy of slip gauges.**

(a) Set M56

1·001 mm to 1·009 mm	by 0·001		9
1·01 mm to 1·09 mm	by 0·01		9
1·10 mm to 1·90 mm	by 0·1		9
1 mm to 25 mm	by 1 mm		25
50, 75 and 100 mm			3
0·05 mm			1
			56

Two protector slips, each of 2·5 mm, are supplied with sets of workshop and inspection grades, but not with calibration and reference grades.

(b)

	49·517	
Protectors	5	
	44·517	Pile is two protectors of
1 + third place	1·007	2·5 mm, 1·007, 1·01, 1·5,
	43·51	16 and 25 mm
1 + second place	1·01	
	42·5	
1 + first place	1·5	
	41	
Excess of 25	16	
	25	

(c) The length of a slip gauge is the distance between one gauging face of the gauge and a metal surface (having a finish similar to the gauge itself) upon which the gauge has been wrung.

The definition of length takes into account the thickness of *one* wringing film which is representative of the actual use of a single gauge.

(d) The four grades are:
1. workshop, for actual production of details, tools, gauges, etc.;
2. inspection, of higher accuracy, for inspection departments;
3. calibration, of even higher accuracy, for use in standards rooms, usually to calibrate measuring equipment in inspection departments;
4. reference, of highest accuracy, usually used for checking other slip gauges.

In general usage, the higher degree of accuracy of reference gauges is so rarely required that the calibration grade usually provides the highest necessary degree of accuracy for ordinary engineering use.

3.10(a) Make a neat sketch to show the approximate proportions of a British Standard slip or block gauge and indicate the gauging faces.

(b) State, approximately, the accuracy requirements for a 20 mm workshop grade gauge block.

(c) Explain briefly how wear in the screw of a 25 mm external micrometer could be detected by using gauge blocks. (C.G.L.I.)

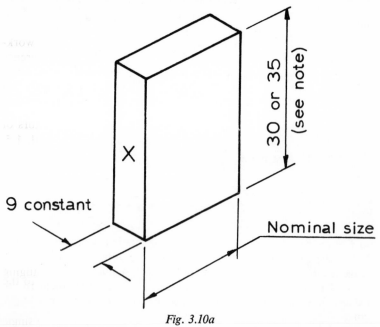

Fig. 3.10a

(a) The proportions of slip gauges are shown in Fig. 3.10. The two gauging faces are at each end of the gauging length. One is marked X on the sketch, the other is the opposite face (hidden in the sketch). The width is 30 mm for gauges up to 4·9 mm nominal length and 35 mm for those above 4·9 mm nominal length.

(b) The accuracy requirements for a 20 mm workshop grade slip gauge, in units of 0·000 01 mm, are

Length	+25 to −10
Flatness	within 25 on each face
Parallelism	within 25

(c) The anvils of the micrometer should be carefully cleaned. Slip gauge piles should be used as the standards of length, and selected so that various positions of the thimble around one revolution are used. A typical initial selection of slip gauges and/or piles could be, in addition to the zero reading

0·5 mm	1 mm	2·1 mm	3·2 mm
4·3 mm	5·4 mm	6·5 mm, etc., increasing by 1·1 mm.	

A micrometer reading should be taken over each pile, using the ratchet on the micrometer to maintain constant measuring pressure. The error in the micrometer reading can then be plotted against the size of slip gauge pile being measured. If sudden changes occur, as could possibly happen with a thread worn at a certain point, further smaller increments could be taken within a narrow range. A calibration chart similar to that shown in Fig. 3.10b may possibly be obtained.

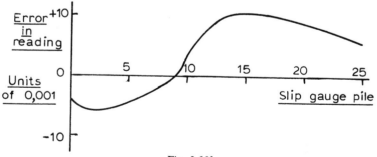

Fig. 3.10b

3.11(a) Describe briefly, with examples, the difference between a line standard and an end standard, as applied to measurement.
(b) State the important feature of slip gauges which makes them of considerable importance in engineering measurement.
(c) Describe how slip gauges and suitable accessories can be used to assist precise marking out.

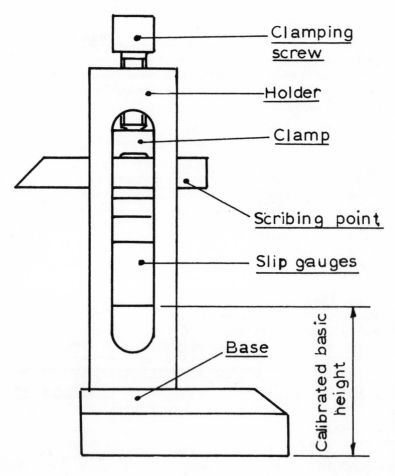

Fig. 3.11

(a) A line standard is a piece of measuring equipment in which length is defined by the distance between engraved lines. A line standard becomes progressively more useful as the number of lengths that can be indicated increases. Typical line standards are rules, micrometers and vernier callipers. An end standard is a piece of measuring equipment in which length is indicated by the nominal distance between opposing faces. A single end standard has but one length only, but different lengths can be obtained by assembling a series of end standards. Typical end standards are slip gauges and end measuring bars.

(b) The important factor is the geometric accuracy of opposing gauging surfaces. The accuracy of flatness enables slip gauges to be wrung to each other to make up a specified length. They can also be wrung to surfaces whose accuracy is of the same order as the slip gauges. The thickness of the wringing films can be discounted in comparison with the overall size of a slip gauge pile. The accuracy is not only that of flatness, but includes parallelism and length. Combinations of slip gauges produce end standards whose length, flatness and parallelism are of a high order of accuracy.

(c) The accessories required would be:
1. a base, similar to that of a vernier height gauge;
2. a holder, whose length depends upon the size of the slip gauge pile;
3. a scribing point.
    The assembly is shown in Fig. 3.11, and would be used in conjunction with an angle plate and a surface plate.

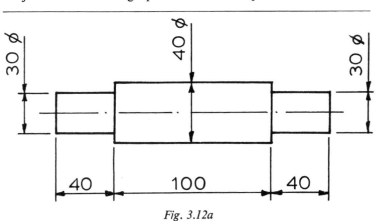

Fig. 3.12a

3.12(a) With reference to the shaft shown in Fig. 3.12a, sketch the methods and label the items of equipment that would be used for checking (i) the concentricity (ii) the roundness, of the 40 mm diameter. State how the magnitude of the errors may be detected in each case. Note that the shaft has no centre holes.

(b) (i) What effect has the radius of the vial of a spirit level upon its sensitivity?

(ii) What is meant by the 'magnification' of a dial indicator.

(N.C.T.E.C.)

(a) Dial indicator set with comparator base, parallels (possibly), slip gauges, vee blocks (or lobing fixture), toolmaker's flat.

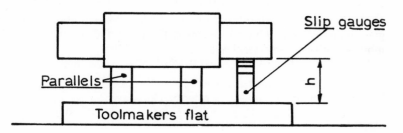

Fig. 3.12b

(i)   Concentricity. Mark a datum angular position on the end of the shaft. With shaft on parallels, datum mark at bottom, try slip gauges to establish height h as shown in Fig. 3.12b. (Parallels may have to be used as the 5 mm difference in radii may not permit convenient variations in slip gauge piles.) Parallels should be dispensed with if possible. Rotate bar, establish height h at say 45° intervals of rotation. Repeat for other end.

(ii)   Roundness. If a lobing fixture (a vee block with adjustable vee angle) is not suitable, use a 90° vee block. Place 40 mm diameter in vee, datum mark at bottom, bring indicator down, clamp at a suitable reading, slowly rotate bar. Repeat with a different angle of vee block if possible (or adjust angle in lobing fixture). Variation in pointer reading indicates lobing. Expressed in a simplified form, variation in the height of pile h indicates variation in concentricity. If total variation is x, *and the diameters are circular*, the amount of eccentricity of the circles is $x/2$. The usual indication is to state 'eccentric by a total indicator reading of x'. Lobing (i.e. lack of roundness) is expressed by the difference of maximum and minimum readings of the dial indicator pointer. Actual figures in each case should be referred to the angular datum.

The above is no oversimplification. The inter-relation of errors in roundness with a determination of errors in concentricity is extremely difficult to assess. Having made the point, time does not allow an extension.

(b) (i) If one end of a gauging surface of length L is raised a distance h above the other, and a vial has a radius of R, the bubble movement x is obtained from

$$\frac{h}{L} = \frac{x}{R}$$

For a given ratio of h/L, an increase in the vial radius R will give an increase in bubble movement x. The larger the vial radius the more sensitive is the spirit level.

(ii) The magnification of a dial indicator is the ratio of the movement of the end of the pointer to the movement of the dial indicator stem.

As an example, suppose the end of the pointer traverses a circle of diameter 21 mm, and a full pointer revolution of say 50–0–50 is in units of 0·01 mm

$$\text{Magnification} = \frac{\pi \times 21}{100 \times 0·01} = 66 \text{ to } 1$$

3.13 A spigot has a diameter of $200 \begin{smallmatrix} -0·02 \\ -0·06 \end{smallmatrix}$ diameter and projects by 5 mm. A recess has a diameter of $200 \begin{smallmatrix} +0·04 \\ +0 \end{smallmatrix}$ diameter and is 8 mm deep.

Describe suitable methods of checking that the diameters lie within limits, giving reasons for the methods chosen. It may be presumed that the spigot and recess cannot be brought together for the measurement.

The tolerance on each feature is 0·04 mm. The nominal diameter of each feature is 200 mm. The ratio of tolerance to nominal diameter is one to five thousand. For accuracies of this order, indicating measuring instruments such as micrometers and vernier, callipers cannot provide sufficient accuracy, and hence comparison methods using gauge blocks should be used.

The wording of the question implies that it is not necessary to determine diameters, but only to determine whether or not the diameters lie within prescribed limits. A 'go' and 'not-go' gauging technique can be adopted.

With articles of this size dimensional changes due to varying temperature could be significant. Once the checking equipment has been set, it should be left in contact with the work for as long as possible, so that the work and the equipment are at the same temperature. When the determination takes place, care must be taken to see that heat from the hand does not affect the determination. It should not be necessary to use gloves provided the determination can be taken quickly. If the articles are of steel, there should be no need to compensate for differential expansion. If they are other than steel it would be advisable to determine modified limits based on room temperature, and that sizes applicable to a measurement at 20°C were determined, so as to compensate for differential expansion or contraction of work and equipment between room temperature and 20°C.

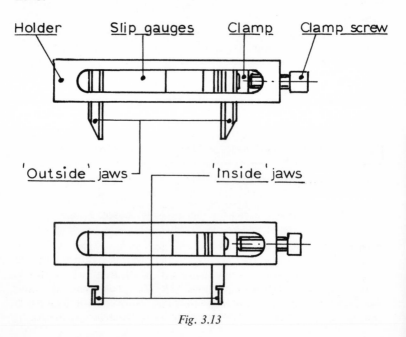

Fig. 3.13

Having accepted existing limits or recalculated new limits, slip gauges and accessories should be used. Fig. 3.13 shows a holder and jaws for use in checking the dimensions.

Slip gauge piles are wrung together and used to position the jaws. For the spigot, one slip gauge pile is wrung for top limit, the other for the low limit. When assembled in the holder, with the 'outside' jaws, the 'go' assembly must encompass the spigot, tried at various diametral positions. The 'not-go' assembly must not pass across the spigot, again when checked at various diametral positions.

With the recess, different jaws are used. The slip gauge piles must allow for the width of two 'inside' jaws. Apart from this a similar 'go' and 'not-go' technique is used as was used for the spigot.

3.14 Describe with suitable sketches, showing calculations where necessary, how the groove shown in Fig. 3.14a would be checked for correct width, depth and angle before removing it from the shaping machine. The component is 250 mm long and has been machined where indicated.

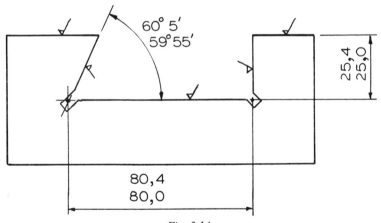

Fig. 3.14a

A mandrel should be rolled on the top surface, and a 25 mm slip gauge should go between the roller and the bottom of the groove. The slip gauge should be tried at a variety of positions. A slip gauge pile of 25·4 mm should not pass between the roller and the lower face of the single dovetail. Once more the slip gauge pile should be tried at various positions. The 80·4/80 dimension is nominal, and this dimension cannot be determined directly. A small roller should be placed in the vee and slip gauges used to find the distance W between the vertical face and the roller. A similar determination should be made with the largest possible diameter of roller, as shown in Fig. 3.14b.

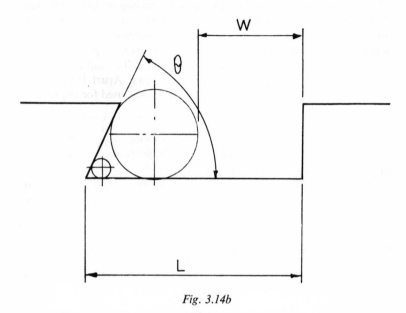

Fig. 3.14b

To illustrate the calculations, assume the rollers have diameters of 10 mm and 30 mm.

With a 10 mm roller

$$L = W_1 + 5\left(1 + \cot\frac{\theta}{2}\right)$$

If a similar determination is made with a 30 mm diameter roller

$$L = W_2 + 15\left(1 + \cot\frac{\theta}{2}\right)$$

Subtracting these equations eliminates L, and then $\theta/2$ (and hence θ) can be determined. Substitution of the value of θ in either equation will give L. The values of θ and then L can be compared with the limits to see if the work is acceptable.

**3.15(a) State six features of the vernier calliper which make it un-suitable for the very accurate determination of large inside diameters.
(b) Name, and briefly describe, a more accurate instrument which uses the principle of a line standard.
(c) Describe briefly the principle of using an end standard to determine accurately an inside diameter.**

(a) 1.   No provision for maintaining a suitable constant measuring pressure, i.e. the force between the workpiece and the measuring faces of the instrument.

2.   Adjustment is not in direct line with the measurement being taken. Deflection may lead to a possibility that the measured distance is not repeated on the scales. This may be aggravated by laxity of the fit of the sliding member on the stock.

3.   The closeness of the engraved lines on a vernier scale do not lend themselves to reading to a greater accuracy than about 0·02 mm.

4.   The flexibility of the stock could lead to an inaccurate esti-mation of the 'feel'.

5.   The radiused jaws used for inside measurement lead to rapid wear.

6.   The length of the radiused portion limits its use to the mouths of holes.

(b) A 'stick' type inside micrometer, consisting basically of a measur-ing head usually having a travel of 25 mm, with end pieces of 25, 50, 75, 150 mm, etc., to build up multiples of 25 mm.

The stick type inside micrometer differs mainly from the conventional inside micrometer in the rigidity of the assembled stick.

(c) An end standard is constructed whose length is a little less than the diameter. A typical example would be to lock a stick micrometer and calibrate its overall length. One end is kept in contact with one side of the bore, and the other is rocked to contact the opposite side of the bore at two points. More accurate determinations are obtained when the 'rocking' is smaller.

The use of blue and dividers should enable the amount of rock '*W*' to be determined within 0·5 mm. This apparent inaccurate determination must be considered in terms of the overall accuracy.

If L is the length of the end standard, the diameter is given by $L + W^2/8L$. $W^2/8L$ is the difference between the diameter and the end standard.

3.16(a) Show, by means of a sketch, the design of a sine bar.
(b) State, without quoting values, the features of the sine bar which have tolerances for accuracy.
(c) What accuracy can be expected from the determination of an angle in the vicinity of 30° with a 200 mm sine bar? Explain how the determination of an angle using a sine bar loses accuracy as the angle grows larger. How is the sine bar usually used if the angle to be determined is close to 90°?

(a)

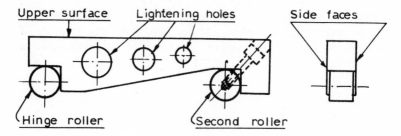

Fig. 3.16a

(b) Upper surface   Flatness
       Side faces   Flatness, squareness to upper surface, squareness to axes of rollers.
       Rollers   Cylindrical accuracy (i.e. taper and lobing), equality of diameters.
       Roller axes   Centre distance, parallelism with each other, parallelism with upper surface

(c) The main relationship of a sine bar is

$$\sin^{-1} \theta = \frac{\text{vertical distance between roller axes}}{\text{centre distance of roller axes}}$$

With a very careful determination, with a 200 mm sine bar, the vertical distance can be determined to within 0·002 mm. The accuracy of $\sin \theta$ is therefore about $\pm 0 \cdot 000\,01$. Taking an average value of say 30°, at this value ± 1 minute is about $\pm 0 \cdot 000\,2$. Hence the sine bar would have an accuracy at say ±1/20 minute or ±3 seconds. The accuracy of determination of an angle using a sine bar is a matter of opinion. Much depends on the accuracy of the ancillary equipment rather than the accuracy of the sine bar, but a reasonable estimation would be that if an angle is required to be determined more accurately than within a minute, the sine bar should be used. The actual accuracy is determined by a specific case. With ground surfaces and precise ancillary equipment the accuracy of determination could well lie within five seconds.

Reverting to a previous statement, let us presume that using a sine bar the sine of an angle can be determined to within ±0·000 01. At zero, the increment in the value of the sine for one minute is about 0·000 3. Hence at zero an angle can be determined to within about 1/30 minute, i.e. within about 2 seconds. At 70°, an increment for the value of the sine for one minute is about 0·000 1. Hence, if the sine can be determined within 0·000 01, the angle can be determined within 1/10 minute, i.e. within about 6 seconds. As the angle nears 90° the increments for one minute decrease, and if the accuracy of determining the sine is constant, the sensitivity of determination decreases.

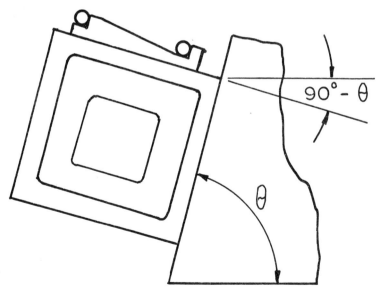

Fig. 3.16b

If the angle to be determined is near to 90°, the sine bar is used in conjunction with a precision square, as shown in Fig. 3.16b, so that the complementary angle, nearer to zero than 90°, is actually determined.

3.17(a) With the aid of a sine bar, slip gauges and dial test indicator describe how to check the angle of the component shown in Fig. 3.17a. (Note: sin 15° = 0·258 8.)
(b) State TWO other methods which could be used to check this angle. Comment on the accuracy expected from these methods. (E.M.E.U.)

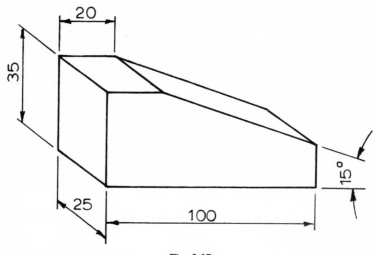

Fig. 3.17a

(a) The set-up for inspection is shown in Fig. 3.17b. A slip gauge pile of 200 sin 15° = 51·76 mm is obtained. (Two 2·5 protectors 1·06 + 1·7 + 19 + 25 would be wrung together.) A 200 mm sine bar would be rested on a surface plate and slip gauge pile as shown, and the block placed on the sine bar with edges matching. A small piece of plasticine would resist a tendency to slide. The dial test indicator would be traversed along the nominal horizontal face of the block. If the block is correct, the pointer would show no movement. If movement does occur, the slip gauge pile is adjusted until no movement of the pointer takes place. If the height of the adjusted pile is x, then $x/200$ is the sine of the angle.

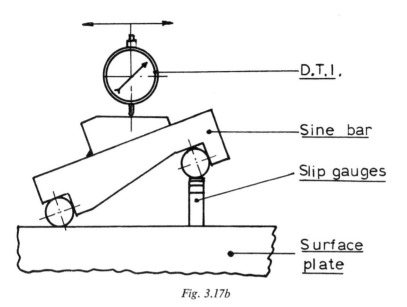

Fig. 3.17b

(b) Two other methods would be:
1. using a combination set fitted with a vernier protractor;
2. using a clinometer, which is basically a vernier protractor with a level.

For method 1 the combination set would be unlocked and the blade moved out a convenient distance. The blade and stock would be positioned to contact the faces at 15° to each other and contact checked by looking through the contacts at a light box after locking. It would be essential to ensure that the 'true' angle is measured by aligning the stock of the set with an edge. The angle is then read off the vernier scales. For method 2 the clinometer is placed on a flat surface in a noted position and adjusted until the bubble reads zero. The initial angular error of the surface is noted. The block is then placed on the flat surface and the clinometer placed on the sloping face, taking care that its new angle is in alignment with the initial error. The clinometer is adjusted until once more the bubble reads zero. The new angular reading is again noted from vernier scales. Subtraction of the initial reading from the final reading gives the angle of the block.

In any measurement, errors occur from three main causes,

viz:
1. quality of the apparatus
2. errors in the setting
3. accuracy of the determination.

The scales of a measuring instrument give little guide to the final accuracy, since individual errors can be cumulative or cancelling. In general terms, and in very general terms, an accuracy can be expected within five times of the smallest nominal graduation of the measuring device, this should include all errors, including those of the set-up. In this case, if the vernier scales of the combination set or the clinometer were engraved to give readings to single minutes, an accuracy of plus or minus five minutes could be expected in the determination of the angle.

Note: An excellent way of checking this angle is with the aid of angular slip gauges, the study of which is outside the syllabus. Nevertheless, the author recommends you to ask your teacher to let you see them, and briefly explain how they can be used with a very simple instrument known as an 'angle-dekkor'. It will make you aware that for the time being you are merely considering the first steps in precision measurement.

3.18   List the equipment required and the procedure to be adopted for the following measurement checks:
(a) the included angle of 24° 45′ shown on the turning mandrel in Fig. 3.18a;
(b) the width of the slots.

(w.j.e.c.)

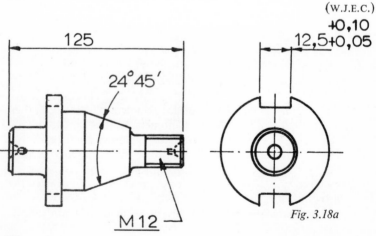

Fig. 3.18a

(a) Equipment:
1. sine centres;
2. slip gauges;
3. surface plate;
4. dial test indicator set.

The detail has centres each end and these could be used for mounting in sine centres. The set-up is shown diagrammatically in Fig. 3.18b.

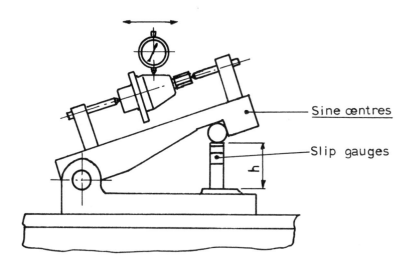

Sine centres

Slip gauges

Fig. 3.18b

Assuming 200 mm centres of rollers, a slip gauge assembly of 200 mm (sin 12° 22′ 30″) would be used. In theory the dial test indicator would be traversed along the maximum height of the detail and no movement of the point would indicate precise accuracy. In practice, the slip gauge pile is adjusted until the pointer reads the same maximum value when the dial test indicator is moved across the detail in several positions. If the height of the slip gauge pile is h, and the roller centre distance is 200 mm, the included angle θ of the taper can be obtained from

$$\theta = 2 \left(\sin^{-1} \frac{h}{200 \text{ mm}} \right)$$

The amount of error can be established and the acceptability (or otherwise) of the taper can be decided.

(b) Equipment: Slip gauges (inspection grade).
A slip gauge pile would be assembled for 12·51 mm. When presented to the slots the slip gauge pile should enter the slots. Another slip gauge pile of 12·55 would be assembled. This second slip gauge pile should not go in the slots. In effect, the slip gauge piles would be used as 'go' and 'not-go' gauges.

The slot (as distinct from the angle) has limits. It is presumed that 'check' implies to inspect whether the slots conform to limits.

If a precise determination of size were required the same technique would be used, but in this case the slip gauge pile would be adjusted to obtain a location fit in the slot, and the size determined by summating the individual slip gauge sizes.

CHAPTER 4

Limits, Fits and Gauging

The questions in this chapter are based mainly upon the following items of the T2 syllabus for Mechanical Engineering Technicians:

Introduction to interchangeability and limit systems; tolerance; limits; clearance and interference; types of fit for plain work, with reference to current British Standards; simple plug, ring and gap gauges for plain work.

4.1 In a modern engineering works, component parts are manufactured from dimensioned drawings. A feature of this method is that some sizes are shown as follows: $\frac{50\cdot03}{49\cdot97}$ when the nominal size is 50 mm hole basis.

(a) Explain why this procedure is adopted and in your answer show that you understand the meaning of the following terms: limits, tolerance, allowance, interference fit and transition fit.

(b) Explain clearly what is meant by selective assembly; when is it used, and how does it differ from interchangeable assembly?

(c) When inspecting cylindrical work a ring gauge or a gap gauge may be employed. Explain the advantages of using both types. (Y.C.F.E.)

(a) An exact size cannot be produced. A deviation from exact size is necessary to allow for unavoidable imperfections in manufacture, and consequently to acknowledge these unavoidable imperfections and also to satisfy the functional requirements of a feature, it is logical to consider that feature as being acceptable if its size (which cannot be measured exactly) is known to lie between a maximum size and a minimum size. A typical manufacturing example is the fit of a shaft in a hole. A nominal size can be given to give some indication of the magnitude, say 50 mm. The basic size upon which the maximum and minimum sizes are determined is usually (but not necessarily) the nominal size. Using a recommended limit system, maximum and minimum sizes can be determined for the hole and the shaft, these being referred to as *limits*. The difference between the limits of a hole is known as the *tolerance* on the hole—the difference between the limits of a shaft is known as the tolerance on the shaft. In particular there will be one limit of the hole and one limit of the shaft which represents the condition where the maximum amount of metal, or other solid, is present. The fit of a hole and a shaft can be controlled by varying the difference of these maximum metal limits, i.e. low limit of hole minus high limit of shaft. This is called the *allowance* for the fit. If this allowance is positive, any hole will be bigger than a mating shaft, and the fit is referred to as a clearance. If the allowance is negative, two conditions can occur. If the limits are so disposed so that ANY shaft is larger than any hole, an *interference fit* results. When the higher shaft limit is greater than the lower hole limit, there is a negative allowance, indicating one condition when interference could occur. However, the other limits may be so disposed that clearance could also occur, depending upon the actual size of a hole and its mating shaft. In such a case, a *transition fit* is said to occur.

(b) Interchangeable assembly occurs when details making that assembly are selected at random, and any selection of parts will produce an acceptable assembly.

Under certain conditions, the limits imposed on an assembly may be so close that, to ensure random selection, the even closer limits imposed on individual details would lead to expensive methods of manufacture. In this case, it is usual to make individual parts to wider tolerances, and then to separate these parts into categories according to their actual sizes. An assembly is then made from selected categories, the process being known as selective assembly. In general engineering usage, selective assembly is not considered to be the *fitting* of details to obtain an acceptable assembly.

(c) The advantages of using gauges for cylindrical work are that the 'go' ring gauge may detect errors that may not be detected by a 'go' gap gauge, such as lobing and raised surface imperfections. If the gauge is sufficiently long, it may also detect bending and drunkenness (i.e. a waved centre line), which again are not revealed by a gap gauge. The advantages of using a gap gauge are that it is faster, it can be used for recesses, and its 'not-go' gap can detect errors which may not be detected by a 'not-go' ring gauge, e.g. barrelling and indented imperfections. In particular, a 'not-go' ring gauge only checks the ends of shafts. A compromise is usually effected by using a 'go' ring gauge with a 'not-go' gap gauge.

4.2(a) With the aid of neat diagrams, give a typical workshop example of each of the following fits: (i) transition; (ii) interference; (iii) clearance.
(b) Choosing *one* example, indicate on a suitable diagram the following features: (i) tolerance (shaft and hole); (ii) high and low limits (shaft and hole).
(c) Name a limit system suitable if large numbers of shafts and holes are received from different sources. (W.J.E.C.)

(a) The fits are illustrated in Fig. 4.2a and, for convenience, the BS recommendation of unilateral hole basis has been adopted.

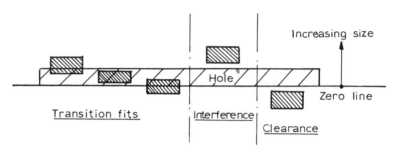

Fig. 4.2a

　(i) With a transition fit interference or clearance can occur depending upon the actual size of a particular hole and its mating shaft. A typical workshop example is the push fit of an electric motor endshield in the motor body.

　(ii) With an interference fit, any shaft is larger than its mating hole and force is necessary to assemble the mating parts. A typical workshop example is the drive fit of a location peg in the body of a drill jig.

　(iii) With a clearance fit, any shaft is smaller than its mating hole. A typical workshop example is the running fit of a lineshaft in a journal bearing.

　Note: Given free choice, the reader should note that a clearance fit is the simplest example to select, but because clearance fits are illustrated elsewhere in this section, the author has selected the most difficult example, that of a transition fit.

(b) Nominal size　40 mm
Unilateral hole basis,　tolerance 0·04 mm

Hole limits   40·04 and 40·00
One shaft limit can lie within hole limits, say   40·02
Other limit can be anywhere, say   39·97 mm
Shaft tolerance   40·02 − 39·97 = 0·05 mm
    The diagram requested is shown in Fig. 4.2b.

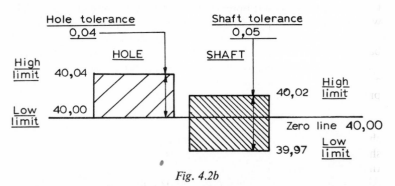

Fig. 4.2b

(c) This question is extremely interesting. The answer depends on time. When it was set (1966) an appropriate answer would be **BS 1916**, interpreted as a unilateral hole basis. Between 1967 and about 1972, answers equally appropriate could be:
1. BS 1916, interpreted on a unilateral hole basis in metric dimensions or
2. ISO recommendation R 268, interpreted on a unilateral hole basis system. After about 1975, an appropriate answer would be the number of the ISO standard which will be issued by then, followed by the statement 'interpreted on a unilateral hole basis system'.

4.3(a) Define the following terms used in interchangeable engineering production: (i) clearance fit; (ii) tolerance; (iii) basic size.
(b) A hole is bored to the limits 50·03 to 50·00 mm diameter and the shaft which is to fit this hole is machined to the limits 50·02 to 49·98 mm diameter. State the allowance for this fit and the value of the maximum clearance. (U.L.C.I.)

(a) (i)   A clearance fit between mating parts occurs when their limits are so disposed that clearance always occurs when any pair made within the prescribed limits is assembled. With a hole and a shaft, the low limit of the hole is always greater than the high limit of the shaft.

(ii) Tolerance is the amount of variation permitted in the size of a feature, such as a linear dimension, an angle, a form, or other design relationship. Tolerance is necessary because of unavoidable imperfections in manufacture and measurement. A tolerance is usually expressed as a difference between limits—for example, a hole with limits of 50·03 mm and 50·00 mm has a tolerance of 0·03 mm.

(iii) Basic size is the theoretical size upon which the limits are based. The sizes of 50·03 mm and 50·00 mm referred to previously were based on 50 mm. Deviations of zero and plus 0·03 to satisfy a particular requirement, together with the basic size of 50 mm, produced the limits stated.

(b) Allowance is the low limit of a hole minus the high limit of a shaft, i.e. the allowance is the algebraic difference between hole and shaft under maximum metal conditions.
In this case,

Allowance $= 50·00$ mm $- 50·02$ mm
$= -0·02$ mm (i.e. a negative allowance)
Maximum clearance $=$ high limit of hole $-$ low limit of shaft
$= 50·03$ mm $- 49·98$ mm
$= 0·05$ mm

(A combination of a negative allowance and a maximum clearance is caused by the limits being those of a transition fit. The limits of the hole and the shaft are so disposed that clearance or interference could occur depending upon the actual sizes of a particular hole and a particular shaft.)

4.4(a) By means of simple diagrams representing the hole and shaft show the essential conditions for: (i) a clearance fit; (ii) an interference fit.

Give a practical example of each.

(b) A steel shaft is made within limits on its diameter of 50·02 and 49·96 mm. State the upper and lower limits of the bore size of a bush to give a maximum clearance of 0·10 mm and a minimum clearance of 0·02 mm. (E.M.E.U.)

(a) Fig. 4.4 shows diagrams giving the essential conditions. The upper portion shows a hole basis system, the lower portion shows a shaft basis system.

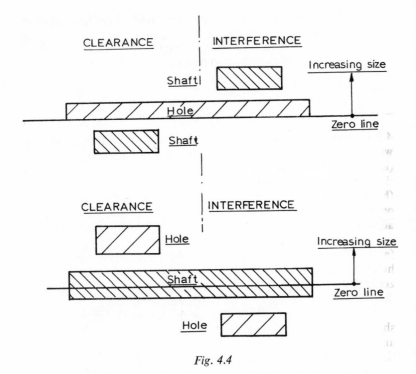

Fig. 4.4

(i) For a clearance fit, the low limit of the hole must be greater than the high limit of the shaft.

(ii) For an interference fit, the low limit of the shaft must be greater than the high limit of the hole.

A clearance fit would be used when the shaft must be smaller than the hole, so that the shaft may rotate freely and a space be available for a lubricant. A typical practical example would be the fit of a lineshaft running in a journal bearing.

An interference fit would be used when the shaft must not rotate and on assembly the shaft and the hole are concentric. A typical practical example would be the fit of a locating peg in the body of a drill jig.

(b)   Maximum clearance = high limit of hole – low limit of shaft
                    = high limit of hole – 49·96
        High limit of hole = 49·96 + 0·10
                    = 50·06 mm

Minimum clearance = low limit of hole − high limit of shaft
0·02 = low limit of hole − 50·02
Low limit of hole = 0·02 + 50·02
= 50·04 mm

Answer.   Limits are $\dfrac{50·06}{50·04}$ mm

4.5(a) Symbols such as H7/p6 may sometimes be used in connection with limits and fits. What is the significance of (i) the capital letter; (ii) the small letter; (iii) the suffix numbers; and (iv) the combination of the symbols such as H7/p6?
(b) Sketch an adjustable limit calliper gauge for plain work. Indicate on your sketch the GO and NOT-GO anvils and show the means of adjustment. (N.C.T.E.C.)

(a) (i)   The capital letter indicates the fundamental deviation of the hole (or internal feature) and determines the position of the tolerance zone of the hole. The fundamental deviation, with the basic size, determines the hole limit which is nearest the basic size.

(ii)   The small letter indicates the fundamental deviation of the shaft (or external feature) and determines the position of the tolerance zone of the shaft. The fundamental deviation, with the basic size, determines the shaft limit which is nearest to the basic size.

(iii)   The suffix numbers indicate the tolerance grades. They are selected when considering the relative precision of manufacturing. Larger suffix numbers indicate larger tolerance grades.

(iv)   A combination of symbols such as H7/p6 govern the quality of the fit obtained when a shaft and hole are assembled. For this particular combination (H7/p6), except for sizes up to and including 3 mm, interference always occurs, but the combination can produce only slight interference. Tolerance grades 6 and 7 can be met by conventional precision machining methods, hence H7/p6 indicates a 'light drive fit' or 'press fit' which can be obtained by routine manufacturing methods.

(b) Fig. 4.5 shows a general arrangement of an adjustable gap gauge. Coarse adjustment is provided by screw A, fine adjustment by a combination of screws A and B. For instance, if A has a pitch of 0·5 mm and B has a pitch of 0·4 mm, one turn in of A and one turn out of B gives a movement to the jaw of 0·5 − 0·4 = 0·1 mm. One-tenth of a turn in of A and one-tenth of a turn out of B gives a move-

Fig. 4.5

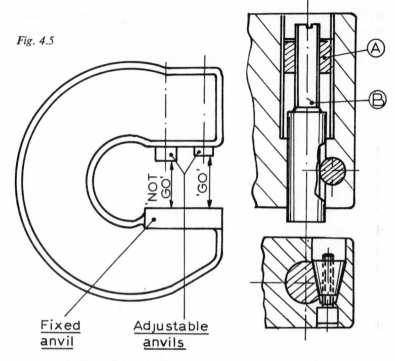

Fixed
anvil

Adjustable
anvils

ment to the jaw of 0·1 mm/10 = 0·01 mm. Once the gauge is set, it is customary to fill in the adjustment holes with wax or a low melting point alloy.

4.6 The following figures are taken from a standard of 'Limits and Fits for Engineering' and refer to a precision running fit for a hole and shaft of 50 mm nominal size:

Hole H7 Limits + 0·025 mm
            + 0·000 mm
Shaft g6 Limits − 0·009 mm
             − 0·025 mm

(a) Draw a simple diagram representing the hole and shaft and on it show, with their values: (i) the hole tolerance; (ii) the shaft tolerance; (iii) the maximum and minimum clearances.
(b) State the actual maximum and minimum sizes of both hole and shaft.

(c) Manufacture could be made much easier by altering the tolerances. What would be the consequences of such an action? (E.M.E.U.)

(a) The required diagram is given in Fig. 4.6.

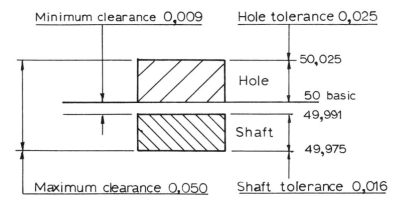

Fig. 4.6

(b) The actual maximum and minimum sizes are

> Hole   50·025 mm to 50·000 mm
> Shaft   49·991 mm to 49·975 mm

(c) An immediate consequence of widening tolerances is generally that of cheapening production. The machine tools and the gauging need not be so accurate.

The consequences on the fit are a matter of opinion, being greatly affected by the actual manner in which the widened tolerances are applied. One must commence by first assuming that the fit must remain a clearance fit and that the allowance of 0·009 mm will be unchanged. In which case, the high limit of the hole would be increased and the lower limit of the shaft would be decreased. It may be concluded that the fit would be considerably eased, but in practice this may not be the case. In actual production, operators tend to keep to lower limits with holes and high limits with shafts and hence, if the allowance were kept, there would be little, if any, change in the quality of the fit if the tolerances were *slightly* increased. Large increases in tolerances could possibly lead to an easing of the fit, which would remain a clearance fit. On the other hand, if the tolerances were widened so that all the limits of the hole and the shaft

91

were modified, the existing positive allowance could be decreased and, if it were eliminated, produce a negative allowance. The existing clearance fit would then be changed to a transition fit.

No firm conclusions can be reached until the actual change of tolerances are specified so that it is possible to calculate new limits for hole and shaft.

4.7(a) A particular 'Limits and Fits for Engineering' recommends the use of a Unilateral Hole Basis System.

   Explain the meaning of the following terms: (i) Hole Basis System, stating why it is recommended; (ii) Unilateral and Bilateral Limits.

(b) In a hole and shaft combination of 25 mm nominal size

$$\text{H7 hole limits are} \quad +0\cdot021 \text{ mm}$$
$$+0\cdot000 \text{ mm}$$
$$\text{e8 shaft limits are} \quad -0\cdot040 \text{ mm}$$
$$-0\cdot073 \text{ mm}$$

State the values of (i) maximum and minimum clearance obtainable,
   (ii) allowance,
   (iii) tolerance on the hole and the shaft. (E.M.E.U.)

(a) (i) A limit system is a system of standard allowances and tolerances, in graded amounts associated with specific ranges of basic sizes, from which, by selection, limits can be assigned to mating parts to provide a particular quality of fit.

   A hole basis limit system is a system of limits and fits in which the different clearances and interferences are obtained by associating various shafts with a single hole.

   The main reason for recommending a hole basis limit system is that the hole cannot be varied conveniently because of the fixed sizes of drills, reamers, broaches, plug gauges, etc., whereas shaft sizes are generally controlled with adjustable cutting or grinding operations and can be measured with adjustable comparators or inspected by adjustable gap gauges. The standardization based on non-adjustable tools provides economies in production.

   (ii) Unilateral limits are obtained by applying a unilateral tolerance to a basic size. This tolerance is a variation permitted in one direction only from the basic size. Bilateral limits are obtained by applying a bilateral tolerance to a basic size. A bilateral tolerance is a tolerance in which variation is permitted in both directions from the basic size, this variation not necessarily being equal in each direction.

(b) Hole limits   25·021 and 25·000
    Shaft limits   24·960 and 24·927
    (i)   Maximum clearance = largest hole – smallest shaft
                          = 25·021 – 24·927
                          = 0·094 mm
        Minimum clearance = smallest hole – largest shaft
                          = 25·000 – 24·960
                          = 0·04 mm
    (ii)   Allowance = maximum metal hole – maximum metal shaft
                          = 25·000 – 24·960
                          = 0·04 mm
(With a clearance fit, the allowance is equal to the minimum clearance.)
    (iii)   Tolerance on hole = difference of hole limits
                          = 25·021 – 25·000
                          = 0·021 mm
        Tolerance on shaft = difference of shaft limits
                          = 24·960 – 24·927
                          = 0·033 mm.

4.8(a) The British Standard recommendation is to adopt a hole basis system. Under what circumstance would a shaft basis system prove more desirable?
(b) Referring to unilateral and bilateral tolerances, what are the significances of: (i) the H fundamental deviation for a hole; (ii) the hole classification Js.
(c) What is a micrometre (sometimes called a micron) and what association does it have with a modern limit system?
(d) State one advantage and one disadvantage of an adjustable gap gauge when compared with a fixed jaw gap gauge.
(e) What is meant by 'allowance for wear' and 'gauge-maker's tolerances'?

(a) A shaft basis interpretation of a limit system may prove more desirable if a long shaft of a single diameter has to accommodate a variety of accessories having different fits, such as pulleys, gears, bearings, couplings and collars.

(b) (i)   The fundamental deviation H is zero. If this is used as the low limit of the hole, the high limit is basic size plus tolerance. The use of the fundamental deviation H is a simple and convenient way of adopting a unilateral tolerance.

(ii) A hole classified Js has no fundamental deviation. The tolerance is equally distributed about the basic size and hence the use of the Js classification is a simple and convenient way of adopting a bilateral tolerance.

(c) A micrometre (or micron) is one-millionth of a metre, that is, one thousandth of a millimetre. Its association with a modern limit system is that it is the unit in which deviations and tolerances are tabulated.

(d) 1. An advantage of an adjustable gap gauge is that it can be reset to various tolerances within its range, and its use is not eventually confined to one specific set of limits.

2. A disadvantage is that it is adjustable, and is therefore subject to the usual disadvantages of adjustable equipment. It must be set and locked with care by skilled operators, and its accuracy needs constant checking. A fixed gauge does not normally require checking at closer intervals than an adjustable gauge.

(e) The constant sliding of 'go' gauging surfaces on details being measured leads to wear, and a wear allowance is made on 'go' gauging surfaces so that the direction of wear makes the gauge wear towards the nominal 'go' limit, so prolonging the life of the gauge. There is no wear allowance on 'not-go' surfaces because theoretically speaking the 'not-go' surface should not slide on the work.

No article can be manufactured to a specific size and hence gauge-making tolerances are necessary, even though the tolerances are considerably smaller than those met with in the production of general engineering details.

Although there are standard recommendations for the magnitude and disposition of wear allowances and gauge-making tolerances, they are by no means universally adopted by industry. Standards are not mandatory, they are recommendations. There is much to commend their adoption, but nothing to prevent their non-adoption when special circumstances dictate.

4.9(a) A limit gauge is required to the following details:

50 mm nominal diameter, class H8

Limits $\begin{matrix} +0\cdot039 \\ +0\cdot000 \end{matrix}$

Sketch the gauge, labelling and dimensioning the 'go' and 'not-go' ends. Wear and manufacturing allowance need not be shown.
(b) State the advantages and disadvantages of gauging a machined shaft by means of limit gauges. (U.E.I.)

(a) The use of the capital letter H for the fundamental deviation indicates that the gauge is for gauging a *hole* having limits of 50·039 and 50·000. Fig. 4.9 shows a double-ended plug gauge, using a laminated plastics handle grip, with case-hardened steel inserts.

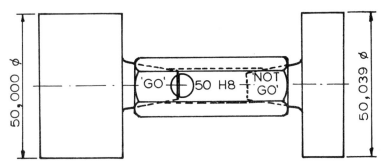

Fig. 4.9

(b) Limit gauges give no indication of the actual size of the detail, they merely attempt to determine whether or not the size of a detail lies between prescribed limits. Their main advantage is that decisions can be made very rapidly. Apart from the minor disadvantage of not determining size, limit gauging does not give a full inspection. Limit gauges may not reveal defects which could be determined by a time-consuming and very expensive complete geometrical inspection—this expense is incurred by the high cost of equipment and the necessity to use highly skilled operatives. For instance, the 'not-go' end of the plug gauge shown previously, although easily used by relatively unskilled operatives, only checks the mouth of a hole, and in addition does not detect lobing. In a similar manner, the 'go' portion of a gap gauge does not detect lobing. When measuring shafts, some improvement can be effected by using a 'go' ring gauge and a 'not-go' gap gauge. For many engineering details, the severity of a full geometrical inspection is uneconomical, and the lack of full accuracy of limit gauging is tolerated in view of the financial savings obtained.

4.10(a) Sketch a 'progressive' type of 'go' and 'not-go' plug gauge, suitable for a 20 H7 hole (limits of 20·021 to 20·000)
(b) State one advantage and one disadvantage of this type of gauge when compared with a double-ended plug gauge.
(c) How can one determine, without measurement or inspecting the marking, which is the 'go' end of a double-ended gauge?
(d) State a suitable material for a plug gauge, including some reference to the heat treatment.

(a) The gauge is shown in Fig. 4.10.

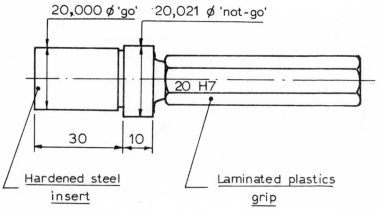

Fig. 4.10

(b) An advantage is that the gauge does not have to be reversed and hence is more rapid in use.

A disadvantage is that it cannot be used for shallow blind holes such as recesses.

(c) The gauging surface of the 'go' portion is normally longer than the 'not-go' portion.

(d) Suitable materials depend on size. For about 10 mm gauging diameter or less, a good quality high carbon steel such as silver steel is suitable. The gauge should be quench-hardened and tempered. For sizes in excess of about 10 mm gauging diameter, a high quality case-hardening steel such as En 38 (5% nickel) would be suitable. The steel should be case-hardened. A plug gauge should preferably consist of gauging portions wedged into a plastic grip by a tapered shank or tapered shanks. Irrespective of the material used for the gauging portions, after the normal heat treatment dictated by the specification of the material, an additional stabilizing heat treatment should be given to minimize change of size with time.

4.11   What is the essential difference between measurement and inspection? The component shown in Fig. 4.11a may be checked by direct measurement or inspected with limit gauges. Illustrate, with neat diagrams, the limit gauges required to carry out an inspection check on this component. (W.J.E.C.)

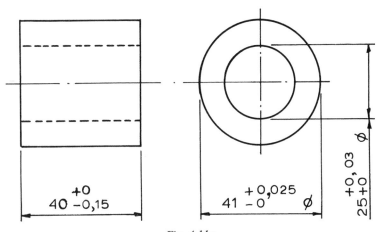

Fig. 4.11a

(a) Measurement is the determination of a size. The acceptance of a feature is then determined by comparing its size with the limits imposed. Inspection, when used in the sense of 'limit gauging', determines whether or not a dimension being gauged lies between prescribed limits, without a determination of size.

(b) One acceptable solution would be three limit gauges:
1. a double-ended plug gauge for the bore;
2. a C-type progressive gap gauge for the outside diameter;
3. a similar C-type progressive gap gauge for the length.
    These gauges are of standard design and readily obtainable from specialist firms; they have been illustrated or implied in other answers in this section. Another solution is shown in Figs. 4.11b to 4.11e inclusive.

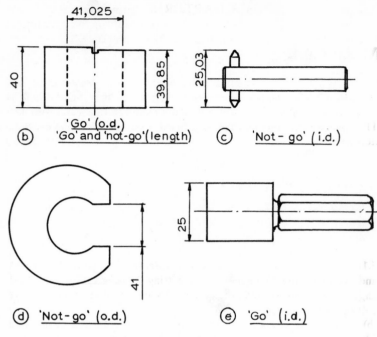

41,025

40

39,85

25,03

'Go' (o.d.)
ⓑ 'Go' and 'not-go'(length)

ⓒ 'Not - go' (i.d.)

ⓓ 'Not-go' (o.d.)

41

25

ⓔ 'Go' (i.d.)

Fig. 4.11b–e

Note: The principle which led to the design of these gauges is a little beyond T2 work. The reader may care to compare this latter solution with that of adopting three conventional gauges, and carry out a little extra reading on 'Taylor's Principle and the design of limit gauges'. At the same time, it should be noted that the drawing gave no limit on concentricity.

CHAPTER 5

Metal Cutting

The questions in this chapter are based mainly upon the following items of the T2 syllabus for Mechanical Engineering Technicians:

Introduction to the theory of cutting tools; forces acting at a tool point; chip produced; effects of top rake and material cut; clearance angle; the standard straight-edged cutting tool.
Heat produced by cutting; use of high speed steel tools.
Effect of cutting fluids; common types of cutting fluid and their application.

5.1(a) Rake and clearance angles are essential to ensure the correct and economic functioning of metal cutting tools. Explain why these angles are necessary and list four factors on which the values of the cutting angles depend.
(b) With the aid of a diagram, show the forces usually acting on a tool when machining a component on a lathe. Explain one cutting tool application where one of these forces does not exist. (C.G.L.I.)

(a) Severance of a chip from a workpiece begins with a wedge being forced into the work material, hence a wedge angle is essential. Referring to Figs 5.1a and 5.1b, the angle A is the wedge angle.

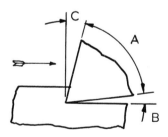

Fig. 5.1a

(a) POSITIVE RAKE

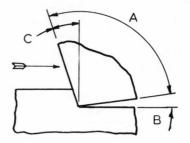

Fig. 5.1b

(b) <u>NEGATIVE RAKE</u>

Angle B is known as the clearance angle and is necessary so that only the leading tip of the tool contacts the workpiece once the chip has been removed. The angle C is automatically decided by the relation

$$A + B + C = 90°$$

and angle C is known as the rake angle.

Fig. 5.1a indicates a positive rake, while Fig. 5.1b indicates a negative rake. The actual removal of a chip depends upon many variables, but in general, when the wedge is forced in, the workpiece is compressed on the tool tip. At a certain load, the workpiece material fails and fracture occurs. With continuous cutting a chip is pared from the workpiece and the leading tip of the tool cleans the workpiece with a scraping action.

The clearance angle B is virtually constant for most cutting tools, being in the vicinity of 5°–10°. This means that the sum of the wedge and rake angles is 80° to 85°. The rake angle is necessary to provide a wedge effect.

Four factors on which the values of the suitable cutting angles depend (one for clearance, three for rake) are as follows:
1. Clearance.
   The geometry of the cutting, to ensure that only the tool tip contacts the work. As already stated the primary value of 5°–10° is generally acceptable. Lower values give increased strength at the tool tip, but when internal boring small diameters, it may be necessary to provide a secondary clearance to avoid fouling the machined surface.

2. Rake.
   (a) The material being cut. In general, the greater the tensile strength the lower the rake, often negative for high-tensile steels.
   (b) The desired tool life. In general, the greater the rake the shorter the tool life.
   (c) The desired surface finish. In general, the greater the rake the worse the surface finish. Negative rake cutting is somewhat akin to reaming.

(b) Any type of cutting produces a single resultant force on a tool point. For convenience, that single resultant force is generally considered to have three components, mutually at right angles, in alignment with workpiece-tool point motions at the cutting point. The components are referred to as tangential, radial and axial, as shown in Fig. 5.1c. With parting off, or forming with a symmetrical

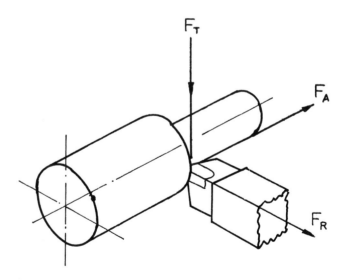

Fig. 5.1c

tool, F_T and F_R are the only components, F_A being absent, as shown in Fig. 5.1d.

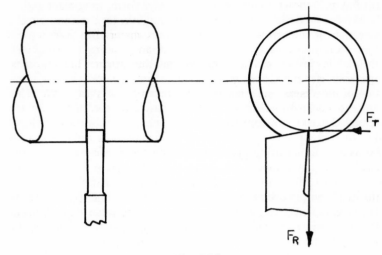

Fig. 5.1d

5.2(a) Draw a neat sectional diagram to show how the cutting point or wedge portion of a shaping or turning tool shears metal.
(b) Of what importance is the rake angle?
(c) Write down an approximate clearance angle for lathe and shaper tools.
(d) Why are certain milling cutters provided with spiral flutes?

(W.J.E.C.)

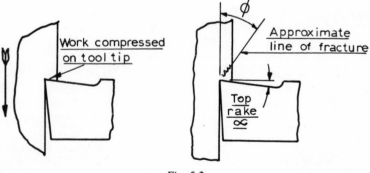

Fig. 5.2

(a) Fig. 5.2. shows a cutting tool, of wedge form, in contact with a workpiece. As the workpiece moves, relative to the tool, in the direction of the arrow, a portion of work material in front of the tool tip is subjected to loading. As with any loading of structures, the load may reach such a magnitude that the structure fails. Broadly speaking, a material fails across a line at an angle of φ to the direction of movement, the angle φ being known as the shear angle. This angle φ may not be clearly defined, in which case the pieces are removed from the workpiece with segmental or discontinuous chips. In other circumstances, φ is clearly defined, and chip removal may be likened to shearing layers which immediately weld together, the chip being continuous.

(b) Representing the rake angle by α, the shear angle by φ, and the coefficient of chip friction as $\tan^{-1} \tau$ (i.e. τ is the angle whose tangent is the force resisting passage of the chip over the tool divided by the normal reaction between chip and tool), many theories have been advanced regarding the relationship between α, φ and τ.

Although there are differences of opinion on the validity of the various theories, subject to certain limitations, as α increases so does φ, decreasing the area being sheared and hence reducing the force to cause shear.

The coefficient of chip friction also decreases, hence so does frictional force, work done against friction is decreased and consequent heat generation is decreased. However, the top rake cannot be increased indefinitely, or the wedge angle would be decreased to such a value that rapid tool wear ensues. The rake angle is important in order to provide a wedging action, and its magnitude is a judicious compromise between conflicting factors.

(c) $5°$–$10°$.

(d) Certain milling cutters are provided with spiral flutes:
1. To ensure that at all times in a revolution of the cutter some cutting is occurring.
2. To have as many different teeth cutting as is possible; (1 and 2 have the effect of reducing the vibratory nature of milling, where chip thickness is not constant, and on occasions during the revolution of a cutter no cutting at all may occur).
3. To obtain a better surface finish with a slicing action instead of a direct wedge effect.
4. To eliminate axial backlash in the arbor by providing an axial

103

component of force to load the thrust bearings.

5.3(a) Outline the machining conditions which generally give rise (i) to a continuous chip; (ii) to a discontinuous chip.
(b) Give two examples of accidents which can be caused by each type of chip, and the precautions which should be taken to avoid them.

(C.G.L.I.)

(a) A continuous chip can be expected when a ductile material (e.g. mild steel) is being cut at a relatively high surface speed (e.g. 2 m/s). Minor conditions which promote the formation of a continuous chip are the presence of effective lubrication between the chip and the tool surface and a generous top rake on the cutting tool.

A discontinuous chip can be expected when a brittle material (e.g. cast iron) is being cut at a relatively slow speed (e.g. 0·2 m/s). Minor conditions which promote the formation of a discontinuous chip are absence of coolant and a minimal (or negative) top rake.

(b) Two accidents which can arise with a continuous chip are:
1. a cut, and
2. a burn

on the hands, when attempting to dispose, by hand, of the hot jagged swarf ribbon. Both can be avoided by using a chipbreaker and a guard acting as a swarf deflector so that the swarf is broken into small lengths and deflected immediately into the swarf tray of the machine. The tendency for a burn can be minimized by using a greater amount of coolant, but cutting conditions may be dry. If a chipbreaker cannot be used, cuts can be avoided by using a rake to dispose of the swarf, with adequate protective clothing, such as gloves. The machine should always be stopped before removing the swarf.

Two accidents which can arise with a discontinuous chip are:
1. a burn when fragments contact the hand,
2. damage to the sight due to a fragment lodging in the eye.

Both can be avoided by the use of a guard acting as a swarf deflector. In addition, adequate protective clothing, such as gloves and goggles, would be an advantage.

5.4(a) Describe what is meant by the following metal turning terms:

(i) built-up edge; (ii) continuous chip; (iii) discontinuous chip.
(b) Give TWO instances in each case of the cutting conditions which influence these effects.
(c) What is meant by chipbreaker?   (N.C.T.E.C.)

(a) (i)   A built-up edge is a small mass of metal adhering to a cutting tool tip, created under certain cutting conditions. It is continually being created and destroyed. Some particles escape behind the cutting edge, appearing as bright specks on the workpiece or, in the case of a badly worn tool, a continuous burnished ring. Some particles disappear with the chip, being loosely attached to its underside.

(ii)   A continuous chip is formed by continuous deformation of the metal without fracture ahead of the tool, followed by smooth flow of the chip on the tool face, with little frictional resistance.

(iii)   A discontinuous chip consists of individual segments which in some cases adhere to each other loosely after the chip has been formed; in other cases they come from the tool as disconnected fragments. The segments are produced by fracture of the metal ahead of the cutting tool.

The chip formations are shown in Fig. 5.4a.

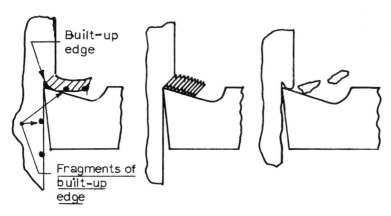

Fig. 5.4a

105

(b) The factors which affect the formation of the various types are mainly:
1. ductility of material
2. speed of cutting
3. friction of chip on tool.

A built-up edge will occur when a (1) ductile material is (2) cut at ordinary speeds with H.S.S. tools. A continuous chip will occur when (1) ductile materials are (2) cut at high speeds with carbide tooling. A discontinuous chip will occur when (1) a non-ductile material is (2) cut at low speeds, irrespective of the tooling.

With the built-up edge and continuous chips friction of the chip on the tool plays a particularly important part. A continuous chip is desirable, and frictional force should be minimized. A coolant with an anti-weld additive such as sulphur will assist, so will an increase in speed and cutting rate.

(c) Although a continuous chip is the most effective form of metal removal, the appearance in the workshop of long continuous ribbons promotes a safety hazard. The continuous chip can be broken into easily managed lengths by a chipbreaker, which curls the ribbons so that they break. A chipbreaker may be a ridge ground on to the tool or an attached piece of hard-wearing material, as shown in Fig. 5.4b.

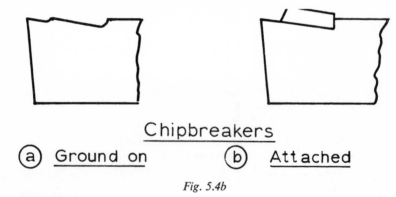

Chipbreakers

(a) Ground on   (b) Attached

Fig. 5.4b

5.5 **When a cutting tool is in use on a centre lathe, the chip produced sometimes turns blue with heat.**
(a) With the aid of a simple cross-sectional diagram of the cutting tool in action, explain how the heat in the chip is generated.

(b) Why must the temperature at the tool point be kept to a minimum?
(c) State two ways in which the heating effect on the tool can be minimized. (C.G.L.I.)

(a) Figs 5.5a, 5.5b and 5.5c show three distinct types of chip which occur when metal cutting on the centre lathe.

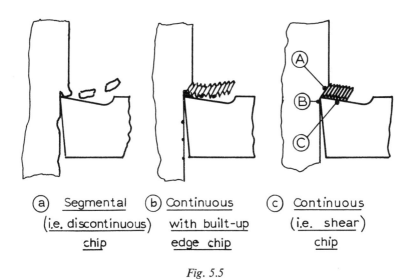

(a) Segmental (i.e. discontinuous) chip   (b) Continuous with built-up edge chip   (c) Continuous (i.e. shear) chip

Fig. 5.5

Irrespective of the type of cutting, there are three distinct features which lead to the generation of heat:

1. distortion within the work material eventually leading to the severance of the chip from the work material;
2. rubbing of the work material as it passes the tip of the tool;
3. rubbing of the chip over the tool after it has left the work material.

If a chip turns blue with heat, the cutting action is most likely to be the continuous chip cutting shown in Fig. 5.5c. Heat occurs from

1. internal friction due to the shearing along line A;
2. rubbing at point B;
3. rubbing along surface C.

107

(b) The temperature at the tool point must be kept to a minimum in order to

1. avoid a detrimental effect on the cutting tool material, such as softening, or the breakdown of the braze on a tipped tool;
2. avoid a rise in temperature of the work, resulting in straining the work and/or machine, producing inaccuracies in the workpiece and the alignments of the machine;
3. promote safer handling conditions for the operator.

(c) 1.   By the use of a copious supply of coolant.

2.   By manipulating the variables in the cutting action, e.g. reducing the cutting speed, reducing the speed rate, reducing the depth of cut, increasing the rake angle, etc.

5.6(a) Describe the equipment and method used in any simple experiment to find the forces acting on a lathe tool during cutting.
(b) Which force mainly determines the power required for machining? What effects do the remaining forces have?   (C.G.L.I.)

(a) The instrument used to determine cutting tool forces when turning is undertaken on a lathe is called a lathe tool dynamometer. There are various models, but the general principle of most of them is to cause the load imposed on the tool to deflect a shape and then to convert this deflection to numerical values of a force or forces. One such instrument has the tool holder connected to a diaphragm, the load on the tool deflecting the diaphragm. Various deflections of the diaphragm are converted to electric currents and these currents are then read on meters. Three meters are used, corresponding to the three components of the resultant. The dynamometer is calibrated by imposing known loads on the tool point (or a replica or a dummy) and observing the readings on the meters. Graphs can then be drawn which enable the load to be determined for a given meter reading.

If necessary, the dummy or replica tool is replaced by the cutting tool. Cutting then takes place and the readings on the meters are noted. Use of the graphs previously mentioned enables the forces to be determined.

(b) Referring to Fig. 5.6, the forces which are determined are F_T, F_R and F_A. If necessary, the magnitude of the resultant R can be determined from

$$R = \sqrt{(F_T{}^2 + F_R{}^2 + F_A{}^2)}$$

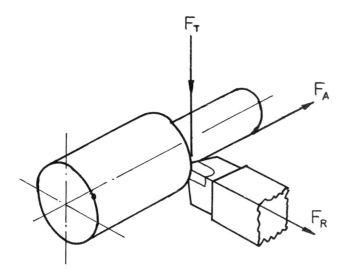

Fig. 5.6

The tangential force F_T mainly determines the power required for cutting. The forces F_T, F_R and F_A tend to distort the machine and the cutting tool, the reactions to these forces tend to distort the work.

For example, force F_T tends to bend the cutting tool and impose a twisting effect on the bed; the reaction causes the work to deflect by bowing. Force F_R compresses the tool and also imposes a twisting effect on the bed; the reaction to this force again tends to bow the work. Force F_A imposes a compressive load on the tail-stock; the reaction to this force compresses the work, and since its direction is parallel to the centre line of the work, it also contributes to a deflection by bowing.

5.7 Describe the main features of any workshop investigation or experiment on either
(a) single point lathe tool or
(b) a twist drill.

The description should cover the following headings: (i) the object of the investigation; (ii) the set-up used, indicating the main items of equipment; (iii) the readings or observations taken; (iv) the information obtained from the observations.

An opportunity will be taken of providing three different answers to this question to illustrate certain aspects of metal cutting.

1. An experiment can be conducted, with reference to turning, with the object of determining upon which component power consumption mainly depends. A lathe tool dynamometer is calibrated and plain turning undertaken with a straight-edged turning tool, the spindle speed, depth of cut and feed rate being constant. The readings taken are

   Set 1. F = tangential component
   D = mean diameter of cutting
   N = spindle speed.

   From these the power consumed due to the tangential component can be determined.

   Set 2. F = axial component
   f = feed rate (length/rev).

   From these, with the spindle speed, the power consumed due to the axial component can be determined.
   No motion occurs in the direction of the radial component, hence no power is consumed.
   The total power = power consumed due to tangential component plus power consumed due to axial component.
   The results should show that under most circumstances, the tangential component is responsible for in excess of 99% of the total power consumption.

2. An experiment can be conducted with the object of determining what effect (if any) cutting speed has on the tangential component when cutting ductile materials when turning in the lathe. A single component lathe tool dynamometer (e.g. the Croydon dial indicator type) is used. This is calibrated by imposing known loads on the tool point. These deflect a beam and the deflection is communicated to a dial indicator. A calibration chart can be obtained which converts dial indicator readings to tangential components. The tool can be a parting tool, which is fed into the work with the surfacing feed of the lathe. At intervals the lathe can be stopped and the diameter of the work noted, with the tangential component immediately previous to cutting that diameter.

   It will be observed that under normal conditions of cutting, variation in the cutting speed has an insignificant effect on the tangential component as long as a continuous chip is generated, even when a built-up edge occurs. It is not until cutting degenerates into segmental chip conditions (rarely obtained under normal cutting conditions) that significant changes occur in the tangential component. At very low speeds, this fluctuates widely, and tends to increase noticeably as the cutting speed nears zero.

3. An experiment can be conducted, reference to drilling, with the object of determining the effect on the opposing torque, at constant speed and feed, of the drill diameter. A drill dynamometer is attached to the table of a drilling machine. The drill dynamometer consists of a body with a concentric turntable. The torque in drilling deflects a beam attached to the body, deflections of the beam being communicated to a dial indicator. The drill dynamometer is calibrated by imposing known torques on the turntable and noting the resulting dial indicator reading. A test piece is clamped to the turntable. One main difficulty is to maintain constant tool geometry of different size drills, and the best that can probably be achieved is to use the products of one maker and grind them on the same setting on a twist drill grinding machine. A spindle speed and feed are selected (based on the mean drill diameter) and are kept constant throughout the test. Starting with the largest drill, the dial indicator reading is noted at the instant of cutting full diameter. The drill is replaced by the next smaller diameter and the procedure repeated through the range of drills.

In metal cutting experiments, relationships of the type

$$A = KB^p C^q D^r \ldots$$

exist, where A is the characteristic being investigated, K is a constant, B, C, D, etc., are variables and p, q, r, etc., are powers.

In this experiment, the torque T is the characteristic and the drill diameter d is the variable, hence

$$T = Kd^x$$

where K is a constant and x is a power.

There is a mathematical method of determining the constants K and d, but if the mathematics are not known, several curves can be constructed with trial values of K and x to find eventually appropriate values. A value of x in the vicinity of 1·8 can be expected.

5.8(a) Discuss the relative merits of high carbon steel and high speed steel as a cutting tool material.
(b) State the types of tools which would be made from these materials and account for the difference in choice. (U.E.I.)

(a) *Relative merits*
Both materials are used for cutting tools because they can be hardened. At room temperature a correctly hardened high carbon steel has greater hardness than a correctly hardened high speed steel. As hardness and wear-resistance are related, at room temperature H.C.S. has greater wear resistance than H.S.S. The tempering range for H.S.S. is higher than that of H.C.S., and is much higher than the temperatures which normally occur when metals are cut. The tempering range for H.C.S. is generally lower. Consequently H.S.S. tools do not lose their hardness when machining metals under normal conditions, but H.C.S. tools tend to soften, particularly if no coolant is used. H.S.S. is a much dearer material than H.C.S., it requires a more exacting heat treatment and is more difficult to machine, hence the cost of tools in H.S.S., both in basic material cost and manufacturing cost, is considerably higher than with H.C.S. Some of the cost difficulties with H.S.S. can be overcome by using cutting tool tips buttwelded to medium carbon steel shanks. The quenching of H.S.S. does not have to be as drastic as with H.C.S., hence the risk of cracking and/or distortion is not so great. As a wide generalization, H.C.S. is preferred for cutting tools under conditions where little or no heat is generated, especially when the material to be cut is non-metallic. The greater proportion of cutting of metallic materials in conventional machining operations is generally undertaken with H.S.S.

(b) *Uses*
High carbon steel tools
Mainly for cutting when little heat is generated (such as when low cutting speeds, low rates of feed and low depths of cut occur), when hardness is important and low cost is desired.

Examples:
Chisels (carpenters' and engineers'), cutlery, guillotine blades, hand taps, hand reamers, scrapers, blanking tools for presswork.

High speed steel tools
Mainly for cutting when heat is generated, and the property of 'red-hardness' (maintenance of hardness at elevated temperatures)

is desired.

Examples:
Lathe turning tools (solid toolbits and buttwelded tipped tools); solid milling cutters, teeth for inserted-tooth milling cutters; drills, reamers and taps for machine use.

5.9 Cutting fluids are required on most metal cutting operations.
(a) State the purpose and requirements of a cutting fluid.
(b) Name the principal types and their applications.
(c) What common additives to cutting fluids are used and why?

(E.M.E.U.)

(a) Cutting fluids are used for one or more of the following purposes. The order of importance depends upon the actual cutting operation, and the following list is not necessarily given in order of importance:
1. To increase tool life by cooling the cutting edge.
2. To decrease tool-chip friction by providing a lubricant between chip and tool.
3. To provide better finish on the workpiece.
4. To reduce forces on the tool and hence economize in power consumption.
5. To cool the workpiece to maintain its dimensional accuracy, by reducing or eliminating the distortion caused by heat generation.
6. To decrease the tendency to form a 'built-up edge'.
7. To flush away chips.
8. To lubricate guiding portions of tooling, such as a drill or pilot in a bush.
9. To discourage corrosion of newly machined surfaces.
10. To lubricate machine movements.
    The requirements of a cutting fluid, once more not necessarily in order of importance, are:
1. The fluid should be an efficient coolant.
2. There should be effective lubrication.
3. Ease of handling, preparation and storage.
4. Optimum service life and minimum cost.
5. No ill-effects on normal machine lubrication.
6. Non-injurious to health (non-toxic, non-fuming).
7. Avoidance of odours.
8. Non-corrosive to machine, tooling or component.

(b) The principal types of cutting fluids are:

1. aqueous fluids;   3. synthetic fluids;
2. oil-type fluids;   4. gaseous fluids.

1. Aqueous fluids are usually emulsions, known as soluble oils. They are generally cheapest and find greatest use where coolant properties are the important factor, such as conventional cutting of metals with high speed steel tools.
2. Oil-type fluids are straight petroleum products, usually known as neat cutting oils or mineral oils. They are generally used when reduction of friction is important and the presence of the water in a soluble oil emulsion is undesirable. Heavy duty cutting can break down the emulsifier of a soluble oil, and the water would tend to flush out the natural lubrication of the machine. Oil-type fluids find considerable usage on automatic lathes.
3. Synthetic fluids form solutions, not emulsions, in water. These solutions are transparent, allowing operators to observe the cutting, and are mainly used on grinding machines.
4. Gaseous fluids, such as carbon dioxide, have limited application, due to high cost, but are occasionally used when liquids have to be avoided, such as when cutting an absorbent material.

(c) The most common additive is sulphur, as occurs with the sulphurized cutting fluids. It is suggested that the sulphur acts as an anti-weld agent, discouraging the formation of the built-up edge and/or reacts with the chip to form solid lubricants on the chip surface. Other additives, usually of a proprietary nature, may be included for one or more of the following purposes:

1. to act as a wetting agent;
2. to discourage foaming;
3. to stabilize an emulsifier;
4. to discourage bacterial growth;
5. to act as a rust inhibitor;
6. to act as an antiseptic.

5.10(a) Explain why it is necessary to use a soluble cutting oil in different dilutions according to the operation and give typical dilutions for (i) milling and for (ii) grinding.

(b) Outline briefly the instructions that should be given to ensure that a soluble oil is correctly prepared for use, and state two precautions which should be taken either during use or in storage to ensure good conditions.

(C.G.L.I.)

(a) Cutting fluids have different duties to perform. In this case a soluble cutting oil is specified, which would normally consist of:
1. a mineral or vegetable oil;
2. an emulsifier, to distribute the oil droplets through the mass;
3. diluting water;
4. additives, such as stabilizers.

In milling, the main purposes of the cutting fluid is to promote good cutting conditions for chip removal, and lubrication between the chip and the cutter is a most important factor. Lubrication is mainly provided by the oil rather than the water.

With grinding, lubrication is of some importance, but it is far more important to cool the work. Cooling is mainly provided by water. Furthermore, in some grinding operations it is necessary to observe the grinding conditions. A greater proportion of oil makes the mixture more opaque. Hence, in general terms, in a basic oil/water mixture, a greater proportion of oil is necessary for a milling operation than a grinding operation.

There is a tremendous range of qualities of soluble oils, and suitable dilutions are often controlled by the efficiency of the emulsifier. The modern tendency is to improve the quality of the emulsifier, so that many dilutions now recommended by oil manufacturers would at one time have been thought unsuitable for milling. If we consider one oil of one manufacturer, the recommendation is one part of oil to twelve parts of water for milling, and one part of oil to fifty parts of water for grinding. Roughly speaking, a dilution for grinding is about four times greater than for milling.

(b) Suitable instructions for preparation would be:
1. Use the dilutions recommended by the manufacturer of that particular oil.
2. Obtain one complete mix at one time, and do not 'top up' either in the storage tank or the machine.
3. Use a softened water, especially if the oil is of vegetable origin.
4. Discard as soon as the emulsifier begins to break down.

Two precautions which should be taken are:
1. In storage, do not contaminate or disturb the mixture by 'topping-up' either with oil or water, or by the introduction of so-called 'reclaimed soluble oil'.
2. In use, ensure that the quantity of supply is adequate. This is especially important in milling, where an insufficient supply of fluid will lead to increased heat generation which, in turn, leads to premature breakdown of the emulsifier.

CHAPTER 6

Machine Tools and Cutting Tools

The questions in this chapter are based mainly upon the following items of the T2 syllabus for Mechanical Engineering Technicians. The actual T2 syllabus content states:

Lathe work; more complex examples of chuck work; faceplate work; use of steadies; taper turning and boring; advantages and use of four-way tool post. Screw cutting; calculation of gear trains for English and Metric pitches; cutting of single-start vee threads, with or without the chasing dial; use of single-point tools and chasers.

Use of drilling machine for spot facing, counterboring and tapping; radial-arm and compound table drilling machines; further examples of setting up work and drilling procedure.

The milling machine: classification of types and uses; identification and function of main features and controls of horizontal and vertical spindle machines; common cutters, their characteristics and mounting; face, slab and side and face milling; form and end milling and slotting; common methods of setting up work; simple indexing; use of rotary table; special safety precautions in use of machines.

(Examiners are not restricted to T2 subject matter in the Part I examination, and certain questions apply to associated topics from T1 work.)

The problems in this chapter deal mainly with the constructional features of machine tools and cutting tools. The use of the equipment is covered in the next chapter.

6.1(a) A lathe has a lead-screw of $\frac{1}{4}$ inch pitch and is supplied with a single set of change wheels ranging from 20 teeth to 120 teeth in steps of 5 teeth. Calculate suitable gear ratios to permit the following threads to be cut on this lathe: (i) 12 tpi; (ii) 32 tpi; (iii) 4 tpi.

(b) Explain why a 127-tooth wheel is often provided in a set of lathe change wheels. (U.L.C.I.)

(a)
$$\frac{\text{Drivers}}{\text{Driven}} = \frac{\text{Lead required}}{\text{Lead of lead-screw}}$$

In this case, the threads are single start (since there are no specific indications to the contrary) and the lead-screw has a pitch of $\frac{1}{4}$ inch. The leads required will be $1/N$ inches, where N is the number of threads per inch.

Hence $\qquad \dfrac{\text{Drivers}}{\text{Driven}}$ (in this case) $= \dfrac{1}{N} \div \dfrac{1}{4} = \dfrac{4}{N}$

The ratios are therefore $\dfrac{4}{12}\left(=\dfrac{1}{3}\right)$, $\dfrac{4}{32}\left(=\dfrac{1}{8}\right)$ and $\dfrac{4}{4}$ ($=$ unity)

    (i) For the 1/3 ratio, a simple train of this ratio, for example an initial driver on the spindle with 30 teeth, final driven on the lead-screw with 90 teeth.

    (ii) For the 1/8 ratio, with a simple train, the smallest driver (20 teeth) would require a final driven gear having 160 teeth. This is not available, hence a compound train is necessary, with products of teeth producing the ratio 1/8.

A suitable combination is

$$\frac{\text{1st driver 30T}}{\text{1st driven 60T}} \times \frac{\text{2nd driver 25T}}{\text{2nd driven 100T}}$$

    (iii) For the unity ratio, a simple train, with the initial driver on the spindle having the same number of teeth as the final driven on the lead-screw, e.g. 50 tooth driver with 50 tooth driven.

(b) The gear train ratio is determined from the equation

$$\frac{\text{Drivers}}{\text{Driven}} = \frac{\text{Lead required}}{\text{Lead of lead-screw}}$$

Let us assume that a metric pitch of lead p mm is to be cut on a lathe having a lead-screw with n tpi (i.e. a lead of $1/n$ inches).

$$\frac{\text{Drivers}}{\text{Driven}} = \frac{\text{Lead required}}{\text{Lead on lead-screw}} = p \text{ mm} \div \frac{1}{n} \text{ inches}$$

$$= p \text{ mm} \div \left(\frac{1}{n} \times 25 \cdot 4 \text{ mm}\right) = \frac{pn}{25 \cdot 4} = \frac{5pn}{127}$$

The 127 tooth gear is therefore used as a driven gear when metric pitches are cut on a lathe having a lead-screw which has a lead of a fraction of an inch.

Note: The reader may care to note that the 127T gear gives precise accuracy, but if this is not available the use of an 85T driver somewhere in the gear train will produce metric pitches with very little error.

6.2(a) Work is being turned slightly tapered in a centre lathe when between centres. Give TWO probable reasons for this and describe how parallelism could be obtained.
(b) Calculate the change gears required from a set ranging from 20 to 120 teeth in steps of 5 teeth on a lathe having a lead-screw of 4 threads per inch to cut a left-hand thread having 19 threads per inch.
(c) Sketch a suitable gear train for (b), connecting the lead-screw to the spindle (assuming that tumbler gears are fitted) and indicate on the sketch the gear teeth numbers and the direction of rotation. (N.C.T.E.C.)

(a) Probable reasons are a matter of opinion and depend upon the amount of use (and/or abuse) to which the lathe has been subjected. Two possible reasons are:
1. accurate centres being misaligned;
2. worn centre or centres.

It would be highly improbable that the misalignment in 1. would be in the vertical plane. Once correct at manufacture there is little subsequent wear to cause a fault. It is more probably due to the tailstock centre not being in line with the headstock centre when viewed in plan. An adjustment can be made to the tailstock centre by means of screws. This allows the tailstock to be moved across relative to the line of centres. (This is done intentionally when taper turning by offsetting the tailstock, and a common error is to reset the tailstock incorrectly after completion of such work, or for the adjustment not to be locked.) 2. may be due to wear or initial incorrect grinding of the 60° angle on centres. After checking that the tailstock centre is hard, its point should be reground on a cylindrical grinding machine. The headstock centre, whether hard or soft, should be ground *in situ* on the actual lathe.

(b)
$$\frac{\text{Drivers}}{\text{Driven}} = \frac{\text{Lead required}}{\text{Lead on lead-screw}}$$

$$= \frac{1}{19} \div \frac{1}{4} = \frac{4}{19}$$

This can be accomplished with a simple train of 20T to 95T, but a gear ratio in excess of four to one is not considered good practice for a spur gear drive. A smoother drive would be obtained with a compound drive.

$$\frac{4}{19} = \frac{8}{19} \times \frac{1}{2} = \frac{40T}{95T} \times \text{any 1 to 2 ratio}$$

The required thread is left-hand. A lathe lead-screw is right-hand. The lead-screw must therefore turn anti-clockwise when viewed from the headstock end, so that when the lathe spindle rotates clockwise, the saddle moves away from the headstock.

(c) A suitable gear train is shown in Fig. 6.2.

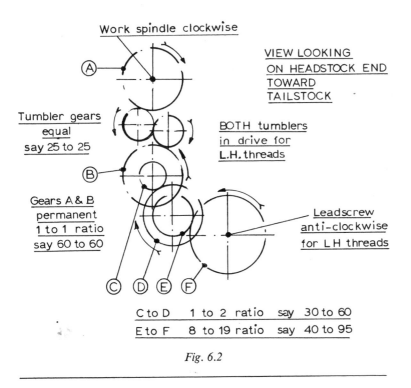

Fig. 6.2

6.3(a) State and compare FOUR different methods of machining external tapers when turning on the centre lathe.
(b) State why it is important for the cutting point of the tool to be level with the spindle centre line.

(a) 1.   Using a plain turning tool in the compound slide, the compound slide being set to one-half of the included angle of the taper, the tool being fed by hand.

2.   Using a form tool, usually in the four-way tool post, feeding by hand.

3.   Deliberately setting over the tailstock so that the centre line of the rotating work lies at an angle of one-half of the included angle of the taper, relative to the centre line of the headstock spindle. Sliding power feed.

4.   Using a taper-turning attachment, the cross-slide lead-screw being disconnected and motion of cross-slide controlled by the slider of the attachment. Sliding power feed.

Method 1 is tiring if the traverse is lengthy, and lack of uniformity in feeding leads to variations in surface finish. The length of the taper may also be restricted to prevent the cross-slide fouling the machine or the work. Method 2 is restricted to short lengths, otherwise chatter will occur. Method 3 should be avoided if at all possible as it deliberately causes an inaccurate alignment which is not easily corrected. Ball-ended centres should be used. Method 4 is not available on all lathes, and the included angle is restricted by the self-locking friction which occurs if a particular angle (for that particular attachment) is exceeded.

The method to be used for turning a given taper, assuming all methods being available on a particular lathe, generally depends upon the included angle and the length of the taper. Very short tapers of any angle are usually produced with form tools. Short lengths of taper not exceeding about 45° included angle are usually turned using the compound slide. Longer tapers not above about 30° included angle favour the taper turning attachment. Very long tapers up to about 5° inclusive may call for offsetting the tailstock.

(b) If the tool point is excessively above centre, the tool will rub and not cut owing to the elimination of front clearance. If the tool can cut, whether it be above or below centre, unless the tool point is level with the spindle true taper will not be generated. (The actual name of the generated solid is a hyperboloid of revolution.)

The error is shown in Fig. 6.3. The tool traverses line BB instead of AA. The distance AA is less than BB, and if the slight variation x can be disregarded, the nominal included angle of the taper produced on the work is less than that suggested by the machine setting.

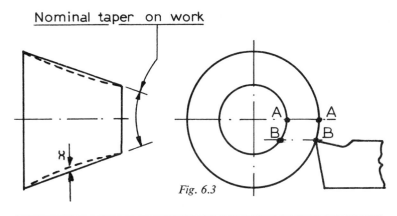

Nominal taper on work

Fig. 6.3

6.4   Make a sketch of a two point lathe steady. State whether this type of steady is of the fixed or travelling kind, giving reasons to support your answer. Give two examples each of the use of: (i) a travelling lathe steady, and (ii) a fixed lathe steady. (U.L.C.I.)

A two point steady is shown in Fig. 6.4.

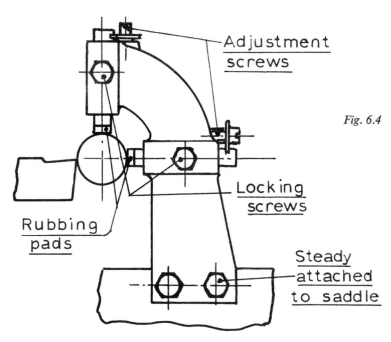

Adjustment screws

Fig. 6.4

Locking screws

Rubbing pads

Steady attached to saddle

In normal use, a two point steady is a travelling steady, because it is fixed to the carriage of the lathe (not the bed). As the tool is traversed along by power feed, the steady moves along, a fixed distance from the tool point. A minor reason is the design. Due to there being two supporting points (as distinct from three of the fixed steady), the work diameter is nominally that of a circle which touches the tool point and the two rubbing pads. To prevent bending, the rubbing pads should be as close to the tool point as possible, and hence should travel along with the tool.

(i) *Travelling lathe steady*
1. Turning a very long diameter, for the majority of its length, in one pass. The steady prevents deflection of the workpiece by providing thrust pads always close to the cutting zone.
2. When support is needed close to the tool in an operation when a fixed steady, with its three pads, would foul the cutting tool set-up, e.g. turning a reduced diameter in a long bar by hand feeding the compound slide.

(ii) *Fixed lathe steady*
Operations conducted on the end of a very long bar, when that bar cannot pass through the hole in the spindle nose, e.g.
1. Tapping the end.
2. Centring.

6.5   Second-operation turning is often done by mounting the work on a temporary mandrel made by turning a peg or spigot.
(a) Give an example of a typical component which could be machined in this way and show a sequence of operations.
(b) A high degree of concentricity can be achieved by this method. Explain the reason for this.
(c) State the main disadvantages of the method and suggest an alternative way of holding the work. (C.G.L.I.)

(a) A typical component would be a plain collar of 45 mm outside diameter, 20 mm inside diameter and 20 mm wide, machined all over, where special reference had been made to a high degree of concentricity between the bore and the outside diameter, and circumstances prevent the two diameters being turned at the same setting.

Operational sequence

Raw material. Sawn-off billet 50 mm diameter, 25 mm long.

1. Grip in three-jaw chuck (stepped jaws). Face across 50 mm diameter. Centre. Drill pilot hole 10 mm diameter. Open out with 19·75 mm drill. Ream bore with 20 mm reamer, floating holder.

2. Reverse in three-jaw chuck (stepped jaws). Face to 20 mm thickness.

3. Use scrap material. Turn a temporary shouldered mandrel to suit bore. Tap end of mandrel. Feed collar on to mandrel, clamp with washer using bolt in tapped hole, turn outside diameter.

(b) The reason for the high degree of concentricity is that the mandrel will be turned on the actual lathe that will be used for turning the outside diameter, and will not be removed until that diameter has been turned. There are no errors of resetting. The turning will also be performed over the same length of bed that was used for turning the mandrel. In effect, the same cutting circumstances occur when turning the mandrel that occur when turning the work, and misalignments of the machine will not affect the concentricity.

(c) The main disadvantage of the method is that in order to feed the collar on to the mandrel some diametral clearance is necessary. A higher degree of concentricity would occur if a hollow tapered hole was produced in the mandrel and the locating portion slotted. Driving in a circular tapered wedge would expand the location equally diametrally to grip the inside of the bore. Great care would be necessary to ensure that the mandrel was not disturbed in the chuck.

6.6(a) Explain why a chaser is often used when cutting threads by single point tooling on the centre lathe. Describe a circumstance when it would not be necessary to use a chaser.
(b) Explain, with the aid of a sketch, the use of a typical chasing dial.

(a) Some threads of vee form (e.g. Whitworth and B.A.) have rounded crests and roots. Even when the theoretical design has flat crests and roots (e.g. unified) the crests and roots are rounded to facilitate manufacture and increase resistance to fatigue. When single point threadcutting it is conventional practice to commence by using a tool of vee form with a rounded tip. The tool has no provision for cutting crests. If rounded crests are desired it is then necessary to follow the single point cutting with a chasing operation.

The fit of a nut on a bolt is theoretically determined by the clearance at the straight flanks. Crests and roots facilitate manufacturing and improve strength, but they should not contribute to the fit. A quite satisfactory fit can be obtained on a threaded assembly if only half of the nominal thread depth is in contact. Taking an external thread of nominal depth 2 mm, the depth can be reduced to 1·5 mm by truncation, i.e. cutting off the crests. If the major diameter were nominally 40 mm, the minor diameter would be 36 mm. Turning the outside diameter to 39 mm but threadcutting a nominal 40 mm thread eliminates the crests and hence a chasing operation is not necessary. This practice is often used to avoid the expense of chasing and wear on screwing tackle, but has the disadvantage of producing a flat topped thread.

(b) A typical chasing dial is shown in Fig. 6.6.

Let us presume the lead-screw A has a pitch of 5 mm, and that the meshing helical spur wheel B has 16 teeth. One complete turn of dial C corresponds to a saddle movement of 80 mm. Each numbered mark on the dial corresponds to a saddle movement of 10 mm as it passes the fiducial mark D. The split nut can engage with the lead-screw at 5 mm intervals of travel of the saddle, hence the split nut can engage at any number, or midway between numbers. In this design, the marks on the dial are noted as 1 to 8 inclusive. To find an appropriate correct cut-in point, the ratio

$$\frac{\text{number on dial} \times 10 \text{ mm}}{\text{pitch}}$$

must produce a whole number so that when the saddle is cut in, the tool is opposite the centre line of the thread form being cut.

As examples,

> pitches of 0·5, or 2 mm, cut in at any line.
> pitch of 4 mm, cut in at even numbered lines only.
> pitch of 8 mm, cut in at lines numbered 4 or 8 only.

Note: The above answer is for a 'metric' lathe. For a 'British' lathe, the lead-screw can be expected to have a pitch of 0·25 inch. Hence one turn of the indicator dial corresponds to a saddle movement

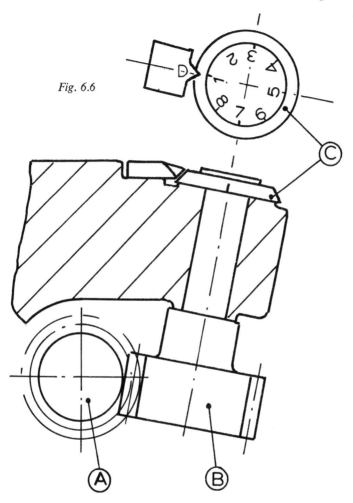

Fig. 6.6

of 4 inches. Each numbered line corresponds to a saddle movement of half an inch. The same reasoning applies, but in this case

$$\frac{\text{number on dial} \times 0.5 \text{ inch}}{\text{pitch}}$$

must produce a whole number,
i.e.

      for even number of tpi, cut in at any number.
      for odd number of tpi, cut in at even numbers only.

6.7   Describe briefly:
(a) Why it is customary to include a four-way tool post as ancillary equipment of a modern centre lathe.
(b) Why do some operators prefer to use (i) a soft centre in the headstock and (ii) a revolving centre in the tailstock when turning between centres?
(c) What is the difference between a 'concentric' (i.e. geared scroll or self-centring) chuck and an 'independent jaw' chuck?

(a) As its name implies, a four-way tool post can accommodate four cutting tools. The body is usually rectangular, and an indexing/clamping arrangement can present each tool to the work. The use of four tools minimizes tool changing. An added advantage is that the indexing arrangement presents a particular tool in the same position each time, and in conjunction with travel stops on the machine, can eliminate continual measurement when repetition work is in production. Hence a four-way tool post is incorporated because it is a useful aid in reducing the time necessary to perform a task.

(b) When turning between centres, the centre in the headstock end is not rubbed by the work, and hence does not have to be hard. If the centre is soft the operative can turn the centre *in situ* on the lathe and hence ensure correct alignment.

At the tailstock end, if the centre were fixed, the work would rub on the centre, and it would have to be hard. Although lubrication is used, the centre tends to wear rapidly, and this may lead to inaccurate workpieces. With a revolving centre, the work does not rub on the centre and wear of the centre is minimal. Furthermore, a revolving centre normally incorporates thrust bearings; these minimize the effect of too great a force on the centre, which could be caused by incorrect initial adjustment or expansion of the work due to heat generation at the tool point.

(c) With the concentric chuck, operation of the chuck key moves all the jaws in or out together. With the independent chuck, operation of the key moves one jaw in or out only, without affecting the position of the others. Concentric chucks usually have three jaws and independent chucks usually have four jaws, but two, three and four jaw chucks of each type can be obtained, as can combination chucks which incorporate concentric and independent movement of the jaws.

6.8(a) Using simple sketches or diagrams, show the following features of a twist drill: (i) the web; (ii) the land: (iii) the cutting edges; (iv) the cutting edge top rake; (v) the cutting clearance.

Which of these features can vary and must be controlled during re-grinding?

(b) The top rake of any cutting tool should be adjusted to suit the metal being cut. Explain how this can be accomplished in the case of the twist drill. (C.G.L.I.)

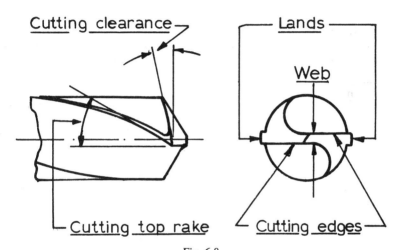

Fig. 6.8

The features required are shown in Fig. 6.8.

(a) (i) The web (thickness) can vary; it increases as the drill wears and the drill is re-ground. It is occasionally controlled when re-grinding, by point-thinning, depending how much of the drill is used.

(ii) The land does not vary and is untouched when re-grinding.

(iii) The cutting edges can vary when re-grinding and should be controlled so that they are symmetrical with a point angle of approximately 118°.

(iv) The cutting edge top rake does not vary for a particular drill. It is fixed by the helix angle.

(v) The cutting clearance consists of two items:

1. the lip clearance angle, which can vary, and should be controlled;
2. the back taper, which prevents the lands rubbing. This is produced when the drill is manufactured, and does not vary.

(b) With a twist drill, the nominal cutting edge top rake depends on the helix angle of the drill. Drills are normally made with either a 'slow', 'normal' or 'quick' helix. These give different rake angles, the 'slow' helix giving the smallest. Presuming a 'standard' drill is being used, to decrease the cutting rake use a drill with a slower helix (i.e. greater lead of the spiral), and to increase the cutting rake use a quicker helix.

6.9   Using simple outline diagrams, explain the difference between radial arm and pillar drilling machines. Show the main motions of each machine, especially how the drill is brought to the centre of the hole. Explain the limitations of the pillar drilling machine.   (E.M.E.U.)

On this occasion it may well be advisable to answer the question in the reverse order to that set. This is a matter of opinion.

There are many designs of pillar drilling machine, and variations in design may well overcome many limitations. However, one feature is virtually common. The plan position of the vertical centre line of the drilling spindle is usually fixed and the spindle only has vertical motion. This means that in plan the work is brought to the drill. The simplest type of pillar drill has a head, a pillar, a base and a horizontal table which can only be raised or lowered. However, pillar drilling machines can incorporate:

1. several parallel pillars, as with the multi-spindle drill;
2. plan position movement to the head, giving some freedom of movement to the plan position of the drilling spindle;
3. vertical motion to the head, as distinct from only feeding the spindle;
4. co-ordinate horizontal table movements;
5. compound tables, giving translatory and rotational movements.

Dealing with bare essentials, the limitation of the pillar drilling machine revolves around the fact that a component has to be moved to obtain a drilling position. Apart from the difficulties of moving heavy components, the size is often restricted by the distance between the pillar and the drill spindle. Many nominal disadvantages of the pillar drill are overcome by using accessories, and simpler radial drilling machines do not have the benefits of angular spindles, compound tables, etc.

Fig. 6.9 shows the basic differences, especially in the method of aligning the spindle with the desired hole. With the pillar drilling, machine work is placed on the table and then moved until it is under the drill. With the radial driller, work is clamped to the table and the drill brought to the work.

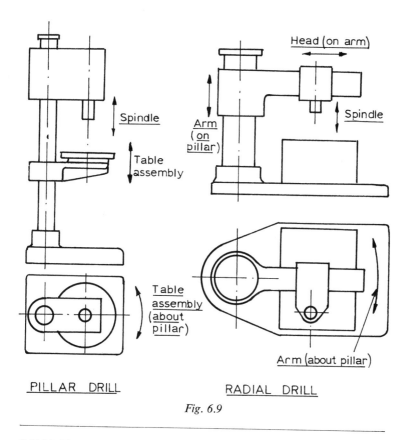

Fig. 6.9

6.10(a) Describe the class of work best suited for the following drilling machines: (i) compound table drilling machine; (ii) radial-arm drilling machine.
(b) Why is it essential to ensure that the tapers on drills and sleeves are clean and free from damage before assembly to the spindle of the drilling machine?
(c) What is the purpose of spot-facing a drilled hole? (W.J.E.C.)

(a) (i) The best class of work for a compound table drilling machine would be where ONE hole only has to be produced, but that hole may involve a combination of one or more of the operations of drilling, reaming, chamfering, counterboring, tapping and spot-facing, preferably using a drill-jig secured to the table, using appropriate slip-bushes and a quick-change collet for the various tools. The whole work operating area should not exceed about a one-foot cube. The benefits of the compound table are rarely used, the capacity of the machine is usually limited by the single fixed spindle.

(ii) The best class of work for a radial-arm drilling machine would be where a multiplicity of holes are required in a single machined face. They could be either plain drilled holes or combinations of two or more of drilling, reaming, chamfering, counterboring, tapping and spot-facing. The work is normally much larger than that accommodated on the compound table drilling machine, and a typical example would be a series of tapped holes and plain locating holes for the sump of a large internal combustion engine.

(b) A taper on a drill has two purposes to serve, that of drive and that of location. If the taper is not clean then the friction would be reduced and the taper could turn in its socket instead of locking and providing a positive drive. If the taper is damaged, projections would affect the accuracy of its fit in its socket and, in addition to the difficulty of providing a positive drive, the tool would be out of alignment with the machine spindle.

(c) A drilled hole is usually spot-faced to provide an accurate seating surface for an engineering detail, such as a washer-faced hexagon-head bolt, which has to be inserted in that drilled hole.

6.11 **A rectangular cast iron base plate 1200 mm × 1000 mm, is received planed on both sides and has a hole at each corner as shown in Fig. 6.11a.**
(a) Specify the most suitable type of drilling machine for producing the holes.
(b) Make a neat sketch of the counterbore tool required showing clearly the cutting edges and their cutting angles.
(c) Describe how the depth of the counterbore can be controlled and measured. (C.G.L.I.)

(a) A radial drilling machine.

(b) Fig. 6.11b shows a counterbore tool consisting of holder, cutter and pilot. The cutter and pilot are chosen according to the dimensions of the counterbore. The cutting is on the end only. There is a slight

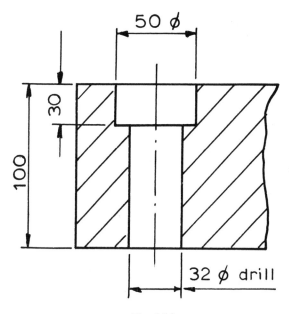

Fig. 6.11a

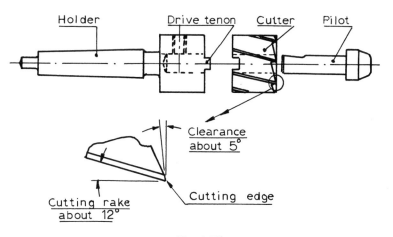

Fig. 6.11b

back-off in diameter from the cutting end. The teeth around the side prevent binding as the counterbore tool is moving into the work, facilitate the cutting of the end teeth when the tool is manufactured and assist in swarf removal.

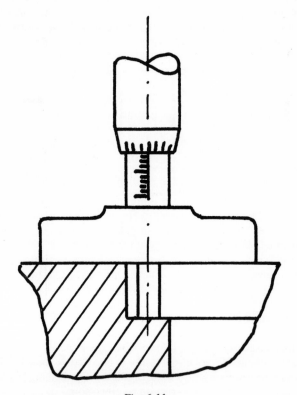

Fig. 6.11c

(c) One way of controlling the depth of counterbore when machining would be to fix stop collars on the counterbore tool. Most operators prefer to use the depth dial on a radial drilling machine. The counterbore tool is lowered to contact the work and the depth indicating dial set to zero. The feed would be by hand and would cease when the dial read 30 mm.

The depth could be measured with a depth micrometer, as shown in Fig. 6.11c.

6.12   Describe how a drilling machine is used for,
(a) hand tapping
(b) machine tapping.

(a) A drilling machine is occasionally used for hand tapping mainly because of the assistance rendered in keeping the tap square— particularly in circumstances which prevent a two handed wrench being used, i.e. where a single handed wrench similar to a spanner has to be employed. It is of considerable assistance if the tapping can immediately follow the drilling of the hole. The drill chuck is removed and a male centre placed in the spindle. The first tap is placed in the hole, the lead roughly locating the tap, and the centre is brought down to locate in a seating centre in the wrench end of the tap. The tap is turned using a wrench on the flats, and as the tap enters the work the centre is kept in the seating by hand pressure on the sensitive feed of the quill. The same method is followed with the second and plug taps.

(b) For machine tapping on a drilling machine a tapping attachment is necessary. Designs of tapping attachments vary, mainly depending upon whether or not the drill spindle can be reversed, and the manner in which overloading of the tap is prevented. With machine tapping it is now quite rare to use a set of taps but rather a 'spiral nose' tap specially developed for the purpose. On one particular proprietary type of attachment, overloading is prevented by a long spring between top and bottom halves, the clicking of a ratchet indicating when the tap bottoms or is overloaded. Extraction of the tap is obtained by reversing the drive to the spindle. A different type gives clockwise rotation to the tap when downward pressure is fed to the attachment, but as the pressure is released, a speeded-up anti-clockwise rotation is used to extract the tap. The changing reaction torque needs a torque arm resting against some fixed part of the machine, and overloading is prevented by a friction drive. The tap is held in a floating holder which means that the tap does not have to be exactly positioned in alignment with a drilled hole. Consequently, when machine tapping several holes of the same size it is more usual to drill all the holes in one operation and then tap all the holes in a following operation.

6.13(a) Identify the main features of a plain horizontal milling machine and explain their function.

(b) Describe with the aid of diagrams, the essential features of three different types of milling cutters and give one application of each.
(U.E.I.)

The main features are shown in Fig. 6.13a.

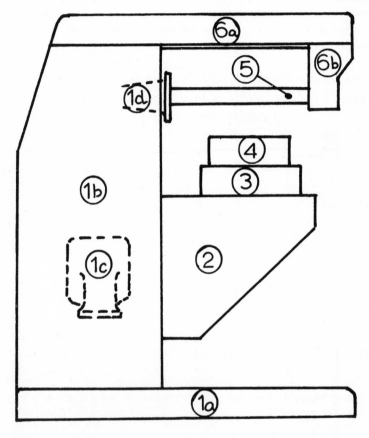

Fig. 6.13a

(a) 1. Main body, consisting of a base (1a) and column (1b). Contains the drive (1c). Top supports the overarm (6a). Side has slide for knee (2). Contains spindle nose (1d) to drive arbor.

2. Knee. Provides vertical movement to table. Usually hand fed.

3. Saddle (or cross slide). Slides on top of knee, towards or away from column (i.e. in line with arbor centre line). Usually hand fed.

4. Table. Slides on saddle with movement at right angles to saddle. Contains tee slots for fixture of work holding. Usually power fed.

5. Arbor. Locates in spindle nose, driven by tenons. Cutter holding device. May be stub or long, in latter case needs support.

6. Overarm and arbor supporting bracket (6b). Used to support long arbors and attachments such as end milling attachment.

(b) 1. Woodruff keyway cutter (Fig. 6.13b).

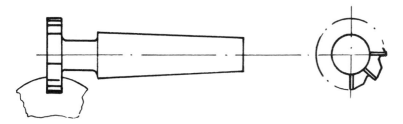

Fig. 6.13b

Used on a horizontal milling machine to cut Woodruff keyways in circular shafts.

2. Interlocking cutters (Fig. 6.13c).

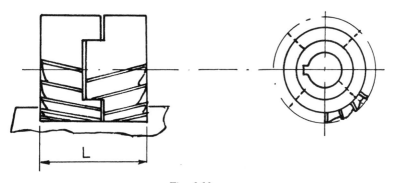

Fig. 6.13c

Used to machine slots where the dimension L needs adjustment on cutters. Used in conjunction with annular shims between cutters.

3. Slitting saw (Fig. 6.13d).

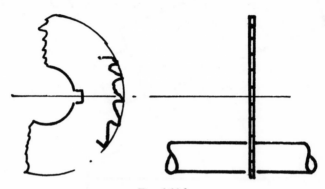

Fig. 6.13d

Narrow disc-type cutter used for cutting off where thickness of cut has to be kept to a minimum. Sides are ground slightly concave to provide a little side clearance.

6.14(a) Sketch or draw clear diagrams of the standard spindle nose of a horizontal milling machine. With their aid describe how arbors are located and positively driven.
(b) Specify a machine and cutter suitable for milling the face BB relative to face AA of the cast iron bearing bracket shown in Fig. 6.14a and, with the aid of sketches, outline a simple method of setting and securing the component. (c.g.l.i.)

(a) Fig. 6.14b shows two views of the spindle nose of a horizontal milling machine.

Arbors are located centrally by the 7/24 taper marked A. This taper is not self-locking (like a morse taper). Arbors are located firmly by a drawbar through hole B pulling the male taper on the arbor into the female taper of the spindle nose. The positive drive is given by the projecting tenons C which engage on slots in the arbor. Certain non-standard special purpose arbors of very large size may

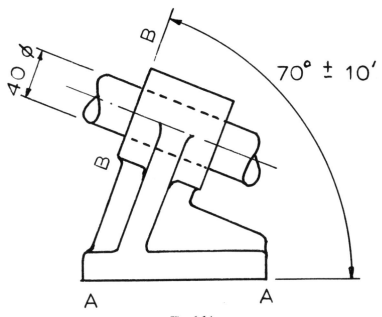

Fig. 6.14a

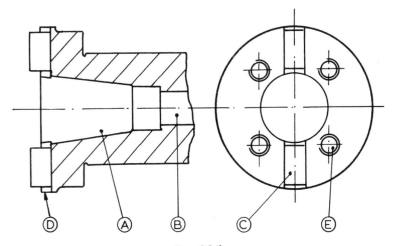

Fig. 6.14b

be located on the spigot diameter D and secured with screws into the holes E. Positive drive is again by the projecting tenons C engaging in slots in the arbor.

(b) It will be presumed that only the base AA has been machined, that machining face BB is the second operation, to be followed by an operation to produce the hole. Use a horizontal miller with a shell milling cutter on a stub arbor and mount the casting on an adjustable angle plate. The angle plate is located on the milling machine table with the aid of tenons in its base, and secured with bolts in the table tee slots. Although the casting is not machined along an edge, machining this edge will provide a useful auxiliary surface for subsequent setting, machining and inspecting. The set-up is shown in Fig. 6.14c.

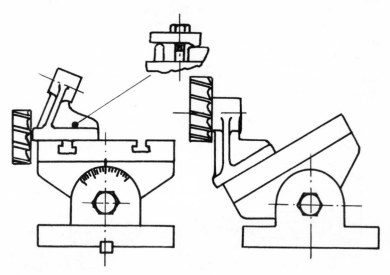

Fig. 6.14c

In the first setting the angle plate surface is checked for parallelism with the machine table with a level, then locked. The casting is rigid and can be clamped with three standard straps using tee slots in the angle plate. A cleaning cut can be taken along the edge as shown in Fig. 6.14c (this is not called for, but it could eventually prove very useful).

The angle plate is unlocked and tilted to a nominal angle of 20° using the graduations on the angle plate. Fine adjustment previous to locking could be obtained with the aid of a clinometer or a sine bar. A cut can then be taken across the boss with a shell mill.

6.15(a) State four precautions which may help to prevent 'chatter' during a milling operation on a horizontal milling machine.
(b) Sketch typical set-ups for (i) gang milling; (ii) straddle milling.
(c) (i)   Name THREE different milling cutters that may be used for milling grooves.
(ii)   Name one type of milling cutter which may be used for milling large vertical faces and the type of milling machine on which it would be used. (N.C.T.E.C.)

(a) 1.   Lock all non-moving slides.
2.   Maintain correct adjustment of moving slides.
3.   Have as many teeth cutting as possible at any one instant, by using helically gashed teeth.
4.   Reduce cutting speeds.

(b) Gang milling a machine bed is shown in Fig. 6.15a, straddle milling a connecting rod end is shown in Fig. 6.15b.

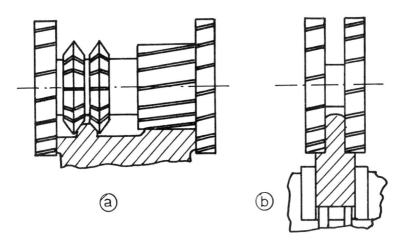

Fig. 6.15

(c) (i)   Three different milling cutters that may be used for milling grooves are:

139

1. staggered tooth side and face cutter;
2. slot drill;
3. end mill.

(ii) Inserted tooth face mill, used on a horizontal milling machine, mounted on a stub arbor, the stub arbor being inserted in the spindle nose of the machine.

6.16   With the aid of sketches describe the working principle of the dividing head, and using this explain how you would index for (a) 56 divisions (b) 1° 30′.   (E.M.E.U)

The main features are shown in Fig. 6.16.

The leading feature of the operation of a dividing head is the 40-tooth worm wheel A meshing with the single start worm B. One complete rotation of the operating handle C thus turns the workspindle D by 9°. The index plate E can be prevented from rotating, and be locked in a datum position, by the plunger F. The index plate carries various hole circles, and by varying the radius of action of the plunger G, various angular spacings which are fractions of 9° can be made. H represents a pair of arms which can be adjusted to assist the correct selection of the number of holes on a particular hole circle.

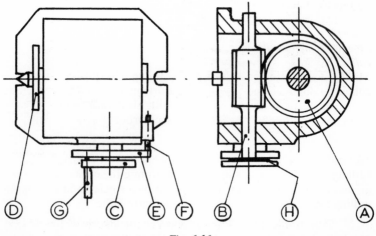

Fig. 6.16

(This answer makes no reference to the use of a dividing head for differential indexing or for spiral milling, these items generally considered as being beyond the T2 syllabus.)

(a) 56 divisions.　　Each division $= \dfrac{360°}{56}$

1 turn of handle indexes 9°.

$$\text{Number of turns} = \frac{360°}{56} \times \frac{1}{9°} = \frac{40}{56} = \frac{5}{7}$$

Any hole/circle ratio of 5/7 will suffice, e.g. 25 holes on the 35 circle or 15 holes on the 21 circle.

(b) 1° 30′.　　Number of turns $= \dfrac{1° \, 30'}{9°} = \dfrac{1}{6}$

Any hole/circle ratio of 1/6 will suffice, e.g. 5 holes on the 30 circle.

6.17　Show, by means of simple diagrams, typical examples of the use of any four of the following cutting tools:
(a) staggered tooth side and face cutter
(b) shell end mill
(c) slot drill
(d) screw thread chasing tool
(e) machine tap
(f) taper reamer.　　　　　　　　　　　　(W.J.E.C.)

(a)	**(b)**
Staggered tooth side and face cutter	*Shell end mill*
Milling a deep slot on a horizontal milling machine	Milling a vertical surface on a horizontal milling machine with shell mill mounted on a stub arbor

(c)	**(d)**
Slot drill	*Screw thread chasing tool*
Milling a shaft keyway, rounded at both ends, on a vertical milling machine	Forming the crests on a thread cut by a single point tooling on a centre lathe

(This nominally answers the question as the problem asked for any four. The following are added for the information of the reader.)

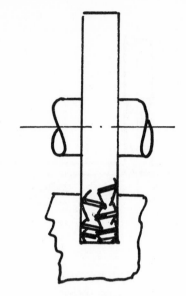

Fig. 6.17a

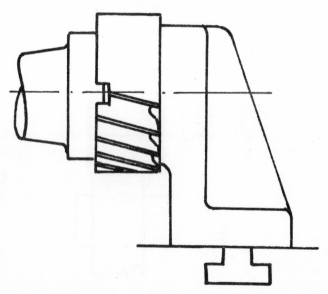

Fig. 6.17b

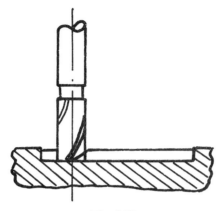

Fig. 6.17c

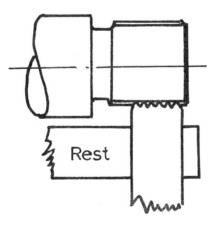

Fig. 6.17d

(e) The description machine tap is interpreted differently in different geographical locations.

Originally it referred to the long stemmed tap used for tapping nuts, the completed nuts being retained on the stem, as shown in Fig. 6.17e. However, the description is now becoming more usually associated with the tap used for any tapping operation on a machine, the initial cutting edges being spiral fluted to deflect the swarf in advance of the tap, with the tap being used in a tapping attachment or in a self-releasing tap holder.

Fig. 6.17e

(f) A taper reamer is used for producing a hole for a taper dowel in a coupling or a taper hole, such as a No. 2 morse taper, in a drilling machine spindle, as shown in Fig. 6.17f.

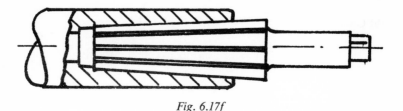

Fig. 6.17f

6.18(a)   Explain why a face cutter is superior to a spiral fluted slab cutter for milling flat surfaces.
(b) An H.S.S. milling cutter 70 mm diameter and having 16 teeth is cutting at a speed of 33 m/min and a feed of 0·1 mm per tooth. Determine the speed in rev/min of the milling machine spindle and the table speed in mm/min. (Take π as 22/7.)   (U.E.I.)

(a) In answering this question, one must refer to generalities: on *most* occasions face milling is superior, but not *always*. One could easily establish a set of conditions where slab milling is not only superior, but essential. For instance, face milling on a horizontal milling machine invariably means the face has to be vertical to the table.

144

However, in general terms, a face mill produces a flat surface by generation, when the accuracy of the resulting surface depends, in the main, only on the accuracy of machine motions. Producing a flat surface by slab milling is basically forming, where, in addition to the accuracy of machine motions, accuracy of the cutter contributes to, or detracts from, the accuracy of the surface. With slab milling, the thickness of the chip varies, while in face milling, the thickness of the chip is constant. Face milling therefore tends to be less vibratory. Slab milling makes use of the arbor, but face milling usually uses a cutter mounted direct to the spindle nose. The greater rigidity of a face milling set-up is generally reflected in the better quality of surface (appearance is not the real measure of the quality of surface texture). The wider intervals between the teeth of a face milling cutter compared with a slab cutter gives easier disposal of swarf and easier application of coolant to minimize the effect of the heat generated in cutting. Actual cutting rakes in slab milling are virtually fixed, but, while face milling, variations in cutting rakes can be easily obtained by slight modifications to tooth angles, such as the inclusion of a chamfered tooth point.

(b) Generally, $$S = \pi DN \quad \therefore \quad N = \frac{S}{\pi D}$$

$$S = 33 \text{ m/min} = 33\ 000 \text{ mm/min}$$

$$N = \frac{33\ 000 \times 7}{22 \times 70}$$

$$= 150 \text{ rev/min}$$

Table speed per min = feed/tooth × number of teeth × rev/min
$$= 0 \cdot 1 \text{ mm} \times 16 \times 150$$
$$= 240 \text{ mm}$$
Answers: Spindle speed = 150 rev/min
Table speed = 240 mm/min

6.19(a) Give an example of a typical form milling operation and explain how a form-relieved milling cutter differs from those with orthodox cutting-clearance.
(b) Explain the main advantages and disadvantages of form milling.
(c) State one alternative machining method for the type of work performed by form milling.
(C.G.L.I.)

(a) A typical form milling operation is the milling of the radius on a block that eventually forms a fork end, as shown in Fig. 6.19.

	Form-relieved milling cutter	Orthodox (e.g. side and face)
Front rake	Zero Leading edge is radial	Usually positive
Clearance	Curved and continuous	Straight, and usually primary plus secondary

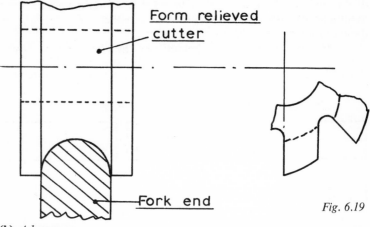

Form relieved cutter

Fork end

Fig. 6.19

(b) *Advantages*
1. Consistency of components, as true form is retained for the full life of cutter by radially grinding the cutting faces.
2. Better appearance of the milled surface when compared with generating.

Disadvantages
1. Each form requires its own cutter.
2. Accuracy depends on cutter form.
3. No opportunity of easing cut with helical flutes, hence a tendency to cause chatter.

(c) An alternative machining method for the fork end shown is generating the radius by slotting, using a slotting machine and a rotary table.

6.20(a) **Why is the feed selection of a milling machine given in length per minute whereas in some machines it is given in length per revolution of the workspindle?**
(b) **A blank for a bolt has a cylindrical head which is to be milled to a hexagonal form on a horizontal milling machine. Briefly describe *two* methods of performing this operation, illustrating your answer with sketches.** (U.L.C.I.)

(a) With a milling machine the feed rates are independent of the rotational speed of the arbor. A change in the rotational speed of the arbor does not change the feed rate of the feeding mechanisms. It is therefore convenient to quote a feed rate in length per minute.

On some machines (a lathe is typical) the feed is not independent of the rotational speed of the spindle. A change in spindle speed automatically changes the feed rate. Hence the feed rate must be quoted in terms of a spindle revolution.

Fig. 6.20a shows diagrammatically the two different drives.

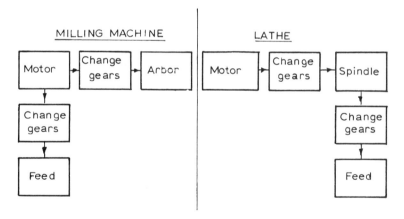

Fig. 6.20a

(b) Two methods are
1. Straddle milling using an indexing device, shown in Fig. 6.20b.
2. End milling using a dividing head, shown in Fig. 6.20c.
1. The device includes a collet for gripping the shank of the bolt. Side and face cutters are used, with a spacer of length equal to the distance across flats. The cutters are set central, a cut is made and the device indexed 120°. Two further cuts produce the hexagon.

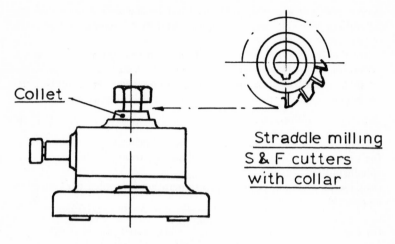

Collet

Straddle milling
S & F cutters
with collar

Rotary indexing collet chuck

Fig. 6.20b

Fig. 6.20c

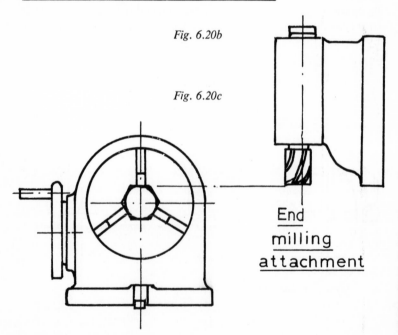

End
milling
attachment

Dividing head with chuck

2. An end milling attachment is used in the spindle nose of the milling machine. The cutter is an end mill, being mounted with its end set one-half of the distance across flats from the spindle of the dividing head. The shank of the bolt is gripped by a chuck mounted on the dividing head spindle. A cut is taken, and the process repeated six times, the dividing head operating handle being turned $6\frac{2}{3}$ times to index $60°$ for each operation.

6.21(a) Sketch and describe one of the following pieces of equipment for use on a horizontal milling machine: (i) rotary table, (ii) vertical spindle milling head.
(b) Give an example of one typical operation for which each piece of equipment can be used. (U.E.I.)

(a) Fig. 6.21a shows a sketch of a rotary table. Designs can vary, but certain features are virtually common. One important feature is tenons in the base lined up with a zero marking on the scale which facilitate setting on the machine. The fiducial mark can be extended to include a vernier scale, but small increments often are obtained by use of dials. On certain models, a lever such as A throws the worm

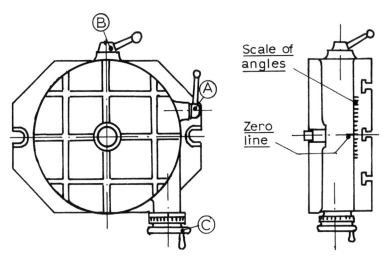

Fig. 6.21a

drive out of engagement for rapid rotation, similar to that of a dividing head. Locks such as B enable the turntable to be locked after a setting. Rotary movement is usually obtained with a worm drive coupled to handle C, which can also have a scale to assist in the obtaining of small increments. With some designs the entire handwheel drive can be discarded and power drive from the lead-screw incorporated. The table slots can be at right angles as shown, or radial. On most designs, a central bush is available which could include a taper, which allows pegs to be inserted for accurate location.

Alternative answer to part **(a)**

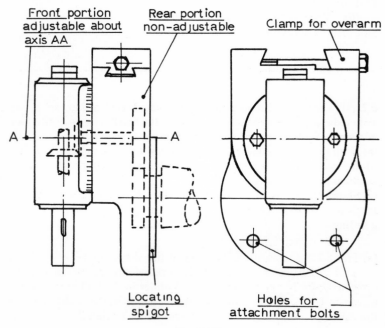

Fig. 6.21b

Fig. 6.21b shows a sketch of a vertical spindle milling head. The drive is provided by affixing a stub arbor into the milling machine upon which is mounted a driving gear. Most vertical spindle heads bolt on to the face of the milling machine column and, in addition, are fixed to the overhead arm for greater rigidity. They usually consist of two portions, one which is rigidly fixed to the milling machine, with the outer portion being able to rotate. The vertical spindle is usually, but not necessarily, at right angles to the table. The two portions enable the spindle to lie at other angles for such operations as cam milling. Smaller sizes use a female morse taper hole in the spindle for cutters, larger sizes and standard 7/24 taper with a draw bar. Vertical motion to the spindle is virtually unknown. Depth of cut is obtained by raising the knee of the machine.

(b) Typical operations are
    (i) Rotary table:
End milling a radiused profile.
    (ii) Vertical spindle milling head:
Slot drilling a keyway, on a horizontal milling machine.

6.22(a) The mechanism of a shaping machine is designed in such a way as to reduce the non-productive portion of the machining operation to a minimum. With the aid of suitable diagrams explain how this is done. (b) With the aid of suitable diagrams, describe, for a shaping machine, (i) the method of varying the length of stroke; (ii) the method of positioning the position of the ram. (c) Show, by means of a sketch, how the clapper box of a shaping machine is set to machine a vertical face and give the reasons for such a setting.

(a) Fig. 6.22a shows a line diagram of the shaper drive.
    The purpose of the design is to reduce the proportion of the cycle occupied by the return stroke. A slider in the bull wheel moves at constant speed. The slider engages in a slot in the main link. On the cutting stroke the slider moves around an angle of θ.

Hence, $$\frac{\text{time of cutting stroke}}{\text{time of return stroke}} = \frac{\theta}{360° - \theta}$$

The pivoting of the slotted link PD at P means that θ is always greater than 180°, hence the cutting stroke always takes longer than the return stroke, and a quick return motion is given to the ram during the non-productive time.

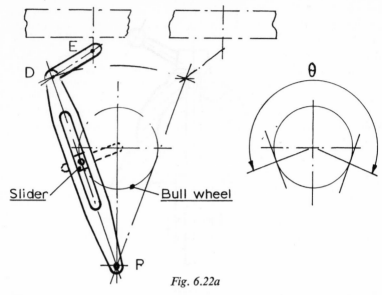

Fig. 6.22a

(b) (i) The length of the stroke is varied by adjusting the radius at which the slider operates in the bull wheel with a mechanism similar to that of Fig. 6.22b. Moving the slider in the direction of the arrow increases the stroke.

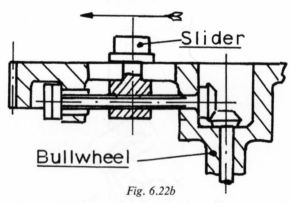

Fig. 6.22b

(ii) The positioning of the ram is adjusted by a simple clamp attached to the end E of the drag link DE shown in Fig. 6.22a. The clamp is shown in Fig. 6.22c. To vary the position, the clamp is unlocked, the ram moved to the desired position and the clamp is then locked.

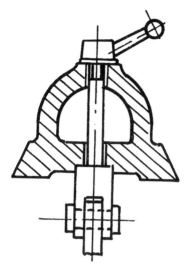

Fig. 6.22c

(c) The clapper box setting is shown in Fig. 6.22d.

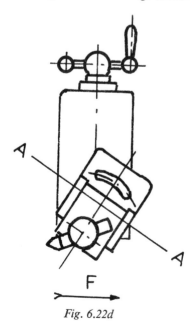

Fig. 6.22d

The reasons for this angular setting are:

1. to prevent the tool rubbing on the return stroke by imparting a lifting rotation about axis AA, hence providing a vector in the direction of F;
2. to prevent undue overhang of the tool when it must be brought to a position to avoid the moving parts fouling the work.

6.23   Describe, with the aid of sketches
(a) a chuck guard for use on a single spindle drilling machine;
(b) a cutter guard for use on a horizontal drilling machine.

(a)

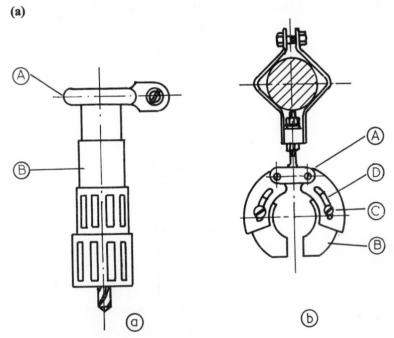

Fig. 6.23

Fig. 6.23a shows a drill chuck guard. It consists of four concentric sleeves which are all adjustable relative to each other. The upper sleeve is fitted with a clip A for fixing to a non-rotating part of the drilling machine, but which has an endwise movement for feeding. Enclosed in sleeve B is a compression spring which allows the guard to telescope when the bottom end contacts the jig, fixture or workpiece. The drill normally projects about 20 mm from the guard when in the raised position so that the initial point of contact can be observed. The sleeves may be of perforated metal or of transparent plastics material in metallic strengthening frames.

(b) Fig. 6.23b shows a milling cutter guard. As shown, the guard is for attachment to a circular overarm, but the guards are available for clamping to other sections of overarm, e.g. dovetailed. The shields have a limited amount of adjustment to suit various diameters of cutter by clamps at the pivots A. The amount of cutter protruding from the guard can be adjusted by radially telescoping the lower portions B and clamping with screws C in the circular slots D.

CHAPTER 7

Manufacturing Methods

The questions in this chapter cannot be associated with any specific portion of a typical T2 or any other syllabus. They are based on the T2 syllabus as a whole, and are used to link up separated portions of the syllabus.

INTRODUCTION

There will always be differences of opinion regarding the so-called 'best method' of producing any engineering detail. These differences of opinion are often brought into sharp focus by the remarkable advances that have recently occurred in the quality and accuracy of machining. Many limits which at one time were automatically associated with grinding are now comfortably held by conventional metal-cutting processes. Furthermore, improvements in the material and design of cutting tools have led to a considerable decrease for the occasions when it is necessary to follow a roughing cut by a finishing cut. The more prevalent process is the removal of all unwanted material in a specific operation in one pass. A finish should never be any better than functional requirements necessitate. The technique often referred to as 'spit and polish' is often a debatable luxury.

There will be even greater conflict of opinion regarding speeds and feeds. It is far more economical to use the greatest power that a machine will provide, and to accept faster tool wear as a natural result. The use of scientifically designed cutting edges and correct tool material will invariably look after finish. The savings in time in almost every case will adequately compensate for higher tool charges. These changes are recognized by examiners, who now rarely request speeds and feeds, these often being dictated by far too many factors for inclusion in a typical question. As a typical example, a grey cast iron is now rarely machined with a slow speed, especially with carbide tooling. Industrial conditions are substantially different from those in the conventional technical college workshop, although there are certain notable exceptions. The student will obtain a considerable amount of accurate information on manufacturing methods by observing those which occur in his place of employment and by reading reputable trade literature.

These remarks should not be interpreted as a suggestion to avoid questions on manufacturing methods. Examiners are skilled, otherwise they would not be appointed. They do not penalize honest differences of opinion. Heavy penalties are the result of illogical sequences, dangerous practices and methods which lead to inaccuracy.

It is interesting to note that the methods suggested in the answers were obtained from a panel consisting of experienced examiners, teachers and planning engineers from industry. The answers are by no means unanimous. The only unanimous opinion is that the answers would earn high marks. Some of the methods are, in fact, contrary to long tradition. Let it be repeated that no reasonable examiner will heavily penalize honest differences of opinion, especially if opinions have equal merit.

7.1   The gear blank shown in Fig. 7.1a is to be machined all over and it is essential that the angular faces are concentric with the 15 mm reamed hole. Describe the setting up and machining of a single component giving sketches where necessary.   (U.E.I.)

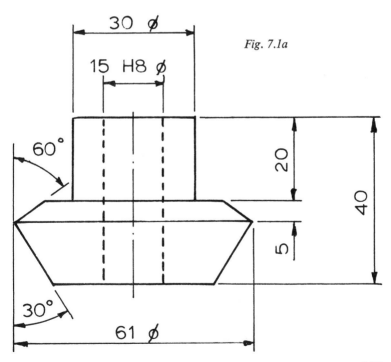

Fig. 7.1a

Concentricity will be achieved by completing the turning in a single setting. The raw material will be a bar of diameter at least 65 mm. The length should be at least 60 mm. Since there is but one component, a random length of bar should be used from store, and the unused material, faced clean, returned to store after use.

Gripping should be in a four-jaw chuck. There is no compulsive reason for the four jaws, but three-jaw chucks cannot be relied upon to provide a substantial grip. It is not necessary to ensure that the gripped bar is running completely true, the detail is machined all over.

A four-way tool post should be mounted on the compound slide, with plain turning tool, plain surfacing tool and parting-off tool.

1. Face across front with plain tool and surfacing power feed.
2. Turn to 61 φ for a length of 30 mm with plain tool and sliding power feed.
3. Start parting off at 41 mm length to provide a recess for taper turning tool to enter, and to leave 1 mm to relieve final parting.
4. Set compound slide to 30°. Turn slower taper. Use plain turning tool of stage 2. Turn until taper starts 25 mm from end. Hand feed of compound slide.

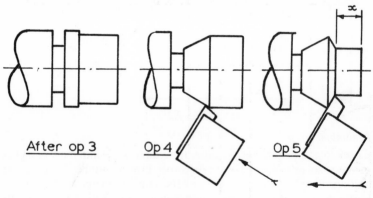

Fig. 7.1b

5. Use same setting to turn quick taper by forming and power sliding feed of saddle until tapers join and dimension x is 20 mm (see Figure 7.1b).
6. Return compound slide to zero and turn 30 φ to 20 length with plain turning tool and power sliding feed of saddle.

7. Centre drill end. Drill 14·75 φ 50 deep. Ream 15 dia 45 deep with machine reamer in floating reamer holder (these three operations from tailstock).
8. Place piece of rod in tailstock and pass into work. Complete parting off to 40 mm length, component after severing to rest on rod and prevent damage to edges.

7.2 **The component shown in Fig. 7.2 is an adaptor to mount a small chuck on the spindle nose of a lathe. Explain in detail how this would be machined all over from a casting. (It may be assumed that the chuck and the lathe are available when the job is being machined.)**

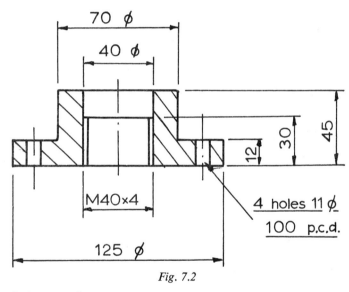

Fig. 7.2

Preliminary work
Check locating diameter on lathe. If possible, ascertain if a stock plug gauge such as a 40H7 plug gauge will give a suitable bore in the casting. If not, turn a soft plug of the same diameter as the spindle location. If an M40 × 4 screw plug gauge is not available, turn a soft M40 × 4 external thread to be used as a gauge. (If the lathe has been in use for a considerable time it would be unusual if these gauges were not available, as they would have been used in making other work-holding devices. They should be made if they do not exist, and retained, as they prove very valuable for manufacturing work-holding devices.)

First setting

(Machine casting to fit on spindle nose.)

Grip with four-jaw independent chuck on 125 φ, adjust to run as true as casting permits, grip tightly.

Tool from four-way tool post. Two plain turning tools (one for surfacing, one for sliding), single point boring tool, single point threadcutting tool.

1. Remove scale from casting by turning and from cored hole by boring.
   Check condition of tools, resharpen if necessary.
2. Turn 70 φ with sliding feed.
3. Turn 70 φ face and 125 φ–75 φ face with surfacing feed.
4. Bore hole to about 35 φ (75% thread depth, truncated thread).
5. Open out to 40 φ, 15 deep, by fine boring, location fit on gauge (or to D.E. plug gauge).
6. Single point thread to M40 × 4 to *very easy* fit on gauge (thread is for holding, not locating).

Second setting

Preliminary work. Check recess diameter of chuck with slip gauges and accessories. Obtain slip gauge and holder set with jaw gap equal to recess diameter. Screw part-machined casting directly to spindle nose.

1. Remove scale from unmachined surfaces of casting by turning.
   Check condition of tools. Resharpen if necessary.
2. Machine 125 φ face with surfacing feed.
3. Machine 125 φ to 'size and size' with spigot diameter.

Drilling

Holes are clearance for 10 φ bolts, should not require vernier marking out. Scribe a diameter with a centre finder from a combination set. Centre pop two holes on this diameter 12·5 from edges. Open dividers to 100$\sqrt{2}$, scribe intersecting arcs. Centre pop at intersections. Check last pair of poppings are at 100 centres. Drill holes 11 φ, radial drill, clamp with washer and stud through bore with 70 φ face on table.

Assembly note Place adaptor in refrigerator, place chuck in warm atmosphere (e.g. shelf of furnace or on a radiator). A 40°C temperature difference will cause diameters to differ by about 0·05 mm. Place chuck on adaptor, allow to reach common temperature and tight fit, assemble with screws.

7.3 **The bearing block shown in Fig. 7.3a has been machined where stated thus** ∇**. Describe the setting-up and machining of the bore on a centre lathe.** (U.E.I.)

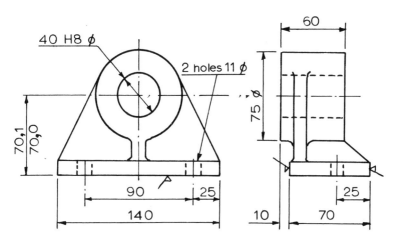

Fig. 7.3a

Equipment required for lathe

Soft centre for headstock, hard centre for tailstock, centred parallel test mandrel (assumed 50 φ), faceplate about 500 φ, right-angle plate, balance weight, boring bar with insert toolbit, gauge for 40 H8 hole (if not available turn a gauge and leave soft), slip gauges.

SEQUENCE OF OPERATIONS

Setting

1. Insert soft centre in headstock. Skim up point by taper-turning from compound slide.
2. Attach faceplate to lathe. Check for true running with dial test indicator, both on rim and face. If faceplate runs out, skim up lightly. (It may be necessary to adjust the lathe to 'gap' bed condition.)
3. Insert hard centre in tailstock after checking point is in good condition.
4. Place mandrel between centres.
5. Wring a slip gauge pile of 70·05 (mid limit) minus 25 (half diameter of mandrel), i.e. 45·05.

161

6. Attach angle plate to headstock and secure in correct position to suit slip gauge pile.
7. Attach balance weight to faceplate at opposite side to angle plate. About 5 kgf at 100 centres should suffice.
8. Line up casting on front edge of angle plate, with boss overhanging edge (see Fig. 7.3b). Clamp by strap clamps after adjusting to best position by noting any run-out of boss and testing with dial test indicator against machined edges at opposing ends of base.

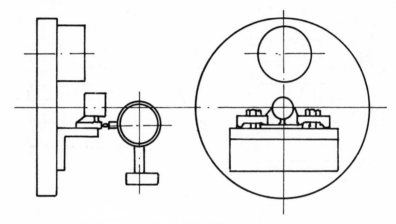

Fig. 7.3b

9. Insert boring bar in tool holder on cross slide. Check position of point against centre.

Machining (Assumed cored grey iron casting, no coolant)
1. Clean up bore, if possible with one pass of boring tool. When bore is clean check condition of tool. Re-grind if necessary.
2. Measure bore with callipers.
3. Rough bore to 39·8 φ approximately, leaving 0·2 mm for fine boring.
4. Finish bore, fine feed, to gauge.

7.4 **The first stage in the manufacture of the collar shown in Fig. 7.4a is to turn a plain ring. A centre lathe fitted with a four-way tool post is to be used. A quantity of 50 is required.**
(a) If the material to be used is mild steel, state the form in which the material should be supplied. Give reasons for your choice.

(b) Using clear sketches show the shape of the cutting tools and their setting relative to the work. Describe a simple operation cycle which will require a minimum of resetting for each plain ring produced.

(C.G.L.I.)

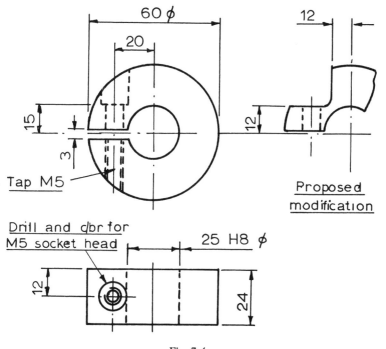

Fig. 7.4a

(a) There are several possibilities for the form of material when turning articles in mild steel to have the form of a ring, the most common being:
1. solid bar
2. billets cut from solid bar
3. pipe
4. forgings.

The main factors affecting the choice are:
1. quantity required
2. dimensions.

For this particular case, the dimensions and quantity exclude the use of pipe, which is generally used for collars of small wall thickness. The quantity required is too small to warrant the cost of tools for forging.

The choice lies between billets and solid bar, and in this case billets would be preferred.

With solid bar the bar must project inside the spindle of the lathe, and the use of billets would enable a smaller size of lathe to be used. Furthermore, unless a long bar is supported at some point other than the chuck, a severe load is imposed on the chuck. When collars are produced from bar, all vestiges of a drilled hole must be removed when one collar has been produced before starting on the next, otherwise the axis of the drilled hole has a tendency to wander. Consequently, the amount of material would be less if billets were used. Parting-off milling is not unreasonably difficult but cutting off billets from solid bar by using a thin abrasive wheel would be much quicker.

The final choice is the condition of the bar. Black mild steel would require a turning operation on the outside diameter. This could, in theory, be eliminated by using bright mild steel. This material is not readily available above 50 mm in diameter, and long storage may require some attention to the outside diameter.

For the quantity desired it would be best to use a length of 60 mm diameter turned steel shafting, readily available from a millwrighting firm, cut off by an abrasive wheel to billets of length 28 mm.

(b) A further advantage of using the material specified is that only one turning tool would be nominally required, but it would perhaps be advantageous to have a tool for chamfering all the edges slightly.

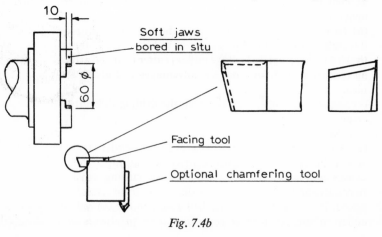

Fig. 7.4b

A three-jaw chuck would be used, fitted with soft jaws. These jaws would be turned *in situ* on the lathe to grip on the 60 mm diameter and provide a register for length, as shown in Fig. 7.4b.

First operation. Turn all collars. Four-way tool post.

1. Set cutting edge to 26 mm from register face, lock saddle.
2. From tailstock, centre drill, drill 10 mm pilot hole straight through, open up to 24·75 diameter, leaving about 0·25 mm for finishing.
3. Face across front, power surfacing feed.
4. Finish bore. Method depends on tooling available.

   Hole is standard size and a standard machine reamer would be used, hand fed from tailstock, held in a floating reamer holder. Otherwise single-point fine bore.
5. Chamfer sharp edges, 0·2 mm at 45°.

Second operation. Turn all collars. Same holding method.

1. Set cutting edge 24 mm from register, lock saddle. Face to 24 mm thickness using power cross feed.
2. Chamfer sharp edges, 0·2 mm at 45°.

(No chamfers are indicated on the drawing, but it is recommended that operations be included to chamfer all sharp edges. A tool could be mounted in the four-way tool post, and be hand fed.

7.5 **After the turning of the ring shown in Fig. 7.4a (previous question) a hole is to be drilled and counter-bored, as shown, to take a pinching screw.**

(a) Explain why it is difficult to drill this hole directly, taking into account the shape and construction of a twist drill and its behaviour under load.

(b) To ease the problem of drilling the hole, it is proposed to mill a flat right across the collar, as shown in Fig. 7.4a, at the same time as the slot is cut. Explain how the milling cutter could be arranged for such an operation, and point out the advantages and disadvantages of this idea.

(c) Suggest any other way in which the drilling difficulty can be overcome. (C.G.L.I.)

(a) A twist drill under load behaves like a slender strut. The loading should be axial. Unbalanced transverse loading at the cutting point causes appreciable deflections. If both cutting edges are cutting normally, as when cutting full diameter, transverse loading is balanced. If it was attempted to drill a hole in the curved surface of the collar in the position shown, the curve produces an unbalanced

165

transverse loading on the point of the drill. Even when the point entered the collar, initially only one cutting edge carries load. These two effects would cause the drill to deflect and the centre line of the hole would tend to lie on a curve. It is highly probable that drill breakage would result due to the drill binding in the hole.

(b) The milling operation would use a 3 mm slotting cutter and a side and face cutter of width about 15 mm, their outside diameters being equal. A collar on the arbor between the cutters would be of width 10·5 mm. The slot and seating would be gang milled. The advantage, apart from producing a flat surface for the drill, is that since the collar has to be slotted anyway, the incorporation of the extra cutter does not unduly prolong manufacturing time.

There are two main disadvantages. There is a pronounced weakness between the vee of the cutaway and the inside diameter. The other disadvantage is that it is highly probable this collar would revolve, and the sharp corners and projecting screw are a grave safety hazard.

(c) The drilling difficulty (and incidentally, the weakness and safety hazard) could be overcome by end milling a recess as shown in Fig. 7.5. The depth would be such that the head of the screw would lie inside the outside diameter.

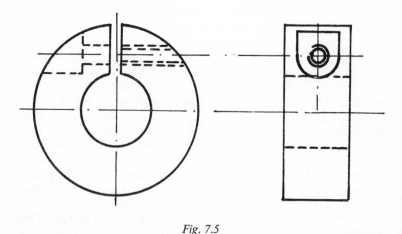

Fig. 7.5

7.6   The component shown in Fig. 7.6 is to be machined on a centre lathe from material 56 mm diameter. The maximum size bar which will pass through the lathe spindle is 40 mm diameter. Describe in detail how the component can be produced.   (E.M.E.U.)

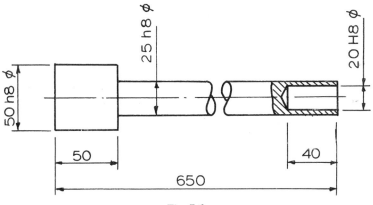

Fig. 7.6

The raw material will probably be *black* mild steel bar about 660 mm long, leaving 5 mm to come off each end. Mark out circular end faces with centre finder, centre pop. Centre each end, deep centres, radial driller, clamping in vee blocks on side of machine table.

First turning

Turn between centres. Rough off to about 32 mm diameter to a length of 605 mm. Turn end to 26 mm diameter, fix travelling steady to saddle, adjust pads to turned diameter, turn to 26 mm diameter for remainder of 605 mm. Increase surface speed, reduce feed and change tool to finish turning tool (carbide tip). Turn to 25 h8 limits for a length of about 20 mm. Adjust pads of travelling steady on this turned diameter. Turn to 25 h8 limit for remainder of 605 mm. Remove travelling steady. Face from 50 φ to 25 φ at shoulder. Mount fixed steady and clamp on bed about 70 mm from small end of job, adjust pads on to 25 φ, remove tailstock centre, and face end to 600 mm length. Centre drill end, drill 19·75 φ to 40 deep, ream 20 H8 with reamer in floating holder.

Second turning

Replace faceplate with collet chuck. Insert 25 mm collet, adjust to grip on 25 φ. Remove component, grip collet, grind to 25 φ with tool

167

post grinder (if collet chuck not available, use concentric chuck, soft jaws, bore out jaws in clamping position to 25 φ).
Pass 25 mm diameter up spindle. Turn to 50 h8 limits remainder of component. Face end to 50 mm length.

    Note: The 50 h8 φ should preferably be turned at the same time as the 25 h8 φ but the lathe would have to be provided with an end driving centre, such as of the Kosta type. This is not a 'standard' accessory for most centre lathes.

7.7   A 50 mm diameter bar 500 mm long is to have a keyway 12mm wide and 100 mm long milled in the centre of its length (Fig. 7.7). Describe, with the aid of sketches, the setting up and clamping of the bar and the positioning of the cutter.   (U.E.I.)

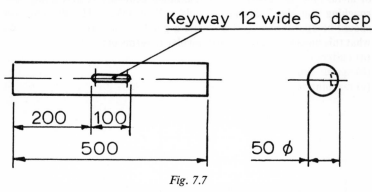

Fig. 7.7

    The keyway slot should be machined on a vertical milling machine using a slot drill. A standard piece of auxiliary equipment for such a machine would be a machine vice, with tenons in its base to ensure that the jaws were in alignment with the table. Standard equipment for such a vice would include hardened and ground jaws for gripping round work, one of which would be plain, the other having a vee.
    The machine vice would have the jaws assembled, and the vice located on the table with the tenons and clamped by bolts in U-shaped slots in the vice base. The slot drill would be set centrally with the component by means of a 19 mm slip gauge from the plain jaw to the slot drill, using the cross-slide screw for adjustment. The cross-slide is then locked and the cross-slide and table are lowered so that the slot drill lies above the work.

The bar is then clamped in the vice, about 120 mm projecting from each end of the vice—this does not affect accuracy as the machining occurs within the vice. The table is then moved so that when measured by a rule, one side of the slot drill is 200 mm from the end. One table tripdog is then set. The table is moved 88 mm (100 mm less 12 mm cutter diameter) and the second tripdog set. The table and cross-slide are then raised until the cutter touches the work, and the dial on the table-raising mechanism adjusted to zero. This completes the clamping and setting, the question does not call for a description of the machining.

7.8   The item shown in Fig. 7.8 is a block of medium carbon steel for a press tool. The face AA is to be milled and a total of about 8 mm of metal must be removed. For maximum economy in machining, one roughing and one finishing cut only will be taken. The finishing cut should be approximately 1 mm and a good finish is required. Explain what this machining process will involve in terms of:
(a) cutters required;
(b) speeds and feeds;
(c) machine settings.   (C.G.L.I.)

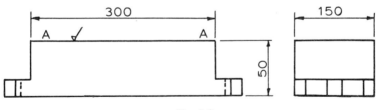

Fig. 7.8

The combination of cutting medium carbon steel, relatively heavy stock removal and high degree of finish suggests the use of a cemented carbide as the cutting tool medium, on a machine specifically designed for such cutting. The following remarks assume that such equipment is available. The block *could* be machined by slab milling on a horizontal milling machine using high speed steel as the cutting medium, but the use of carbide tooling would be far superior.

(a) The cutter would be of the inserted-tooth type, its general form that of a shell mill. The cutters would operate at about 200 mm

169

diameter, and there would be about twelve inserts in the cutter-body. The actual cutting rake would be negative. A vertical milling machine should be used, having extremely robust construction and a motor of adequate power. The same cutter could be used for both operations.

(b) Both roughing and finishing would be undertaken at about 60 m/min surface speed (about 100 rev/min spindle speed). The feed/tooth should be about 0·25 mm. With a 12-tooth cutter this gives a feed of no less than about 300 mm/min.

(c) The method chosen gives extreme simplicity in machine setting. Presuming that the base has already been machined, the bolster block would be bolted straight on to the machine table, using the slots in the end of the bolster. The general rigidity of the bolster block should require no further clamping, but if necessary, additional thrust blocks could be clamped to the table to take the cutting forces imposed, and these would rest against the side of the bolster. The centre line of the cutter would be aligned roughly with the centre of the block, with its cutting tool points initially set 51 mm above the table. It is essential to cut dry, and considerable care should be taken with guarding as the chips leave the work in small curls of appreciable weight at great velocity. The finish after the first cut should be noted. The type of cutting produces a finish of high quality, which should be satisfactory for the final surface, but if a better finish is desired, the cutting speed could be increased and the rate of feed diminished for the final cut. The table is raised by 1 mm for the finishing operation.

7.9   Briefly explain and illustrate how you would machine the brass casting shown in Fig. 7.9a to ensure:
(a) symmetry;
(b) correct intersection of the axes of 20 φ bore and 10 φ holes.

1. Using a four-jaw chuck, gripping on the solid 59 × 35 rectangular section, the boss would be faced, turned 35 φ 20 long, and the rectangular face turned. The 20 φ hole may or may not be cored. If it is not cored, the boss should be centred, drilled with a 5 φ pilot drill and drilled 19·75 φ and reamed 20 φ. (If the hole is cored, single point boring should be used instead of drilling.) The turning operations are indicated in Fig. 7.9b.
2. The milling will be carried out with the aid of a dividing head (or a similar rotary indexing device). The clamping chosen depends on

the equipment available. The best is an expanding plug in the 20 φ hole. Alternatively, soft jaws or a collet could grip on the 35 φ or a mandrel and washer could be used with the 20 φ bore, noting that the clearance between the milling cutter and the clamping washer would be rather small. Although not needed for

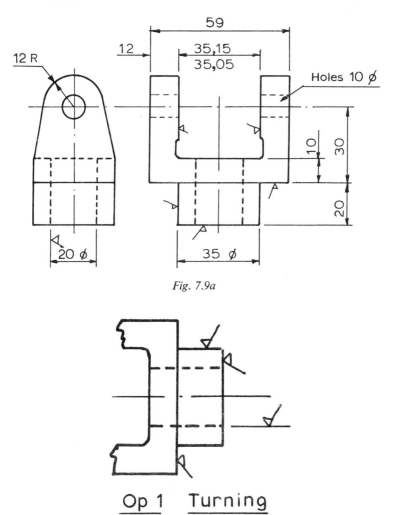

Fig. 7.9a

Op 1 Turning

Fig. 7.9b

this operation, the arbor centre should be adjusted to the same height as the dividing head axis to facilitate operation 3. This can be done with the aid of a mandrel in the dividing head of the same diameter as the arbor. A side and face cutter should be used to clean up one face inside the fork, and the dividing head indexed through 180°, so that the same face of the cutter machines the other inside face of the fork. (See Fig. 7.9c.) The width between

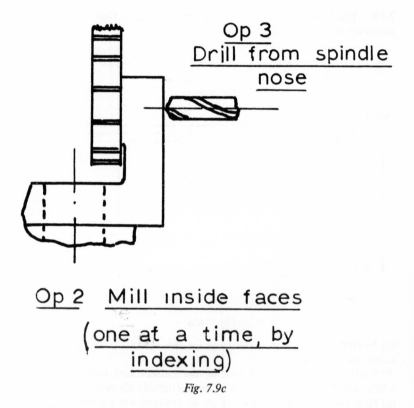

Op 3
Drill from spindle
nose

Op 2   Mill inside faces
(one at a time, by
indexing)

Fig. 7.9c

the forks should now be checked with slip gauges, the cross slide moved a required amount and the operation repeated to produce a nominal width of 35·1 mm. The slot is now symmetrical with the hole and the faces geometrically correct with the axis of the hole.

172

3 Leaving the setting as it is, replace the arbor assembly by a drill chuck mounted direct into the spindle nose of the milling machine. Adjust table position to 30 mm distance. Centre drill and drill 10 mm one lug, using hand feed on cross slide. Index component through 180°, centre drill and drill other lug. The holes are now geometrically symmetrical with reference to the fork faces and the axis of the holes intersects the axis of the boss.

7.10   The 200 mm long cast iron component (Fig. 7.10a) is to be gang milled on the surfaces indicated.

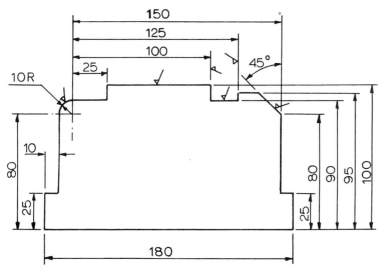

Fig. 7.10a

(a) Sketch the set-up of the cutters for this operation and label their names on the sketch.
(b) State the outside diameters of the cutters and their minimum widths assuming the smallest cutter has an outside diameter of 100 mm.
(c) How could a tendency to chatter be reduced when using the gang milling method?   (w.j.e.c.)

(a) A is a double corner rounding cutter
    B is a helical slab mill
    C is a staggered tooth side-and-face mill
    D is a double 45° angle cutter

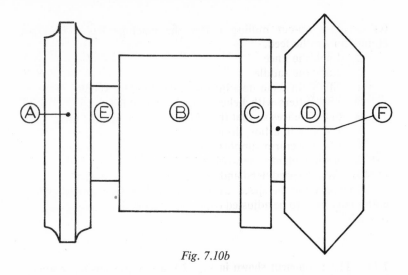

Fig. 7.10b

E and F are spacing collars which may or may not be required. (A and D could be single—but this imposes a restriction on the direction of rotation, and down-cut (i.e. climb milling) should be avoided unless the machine has a backlash eliminator.)

(b) Start with *Cutter B*.

Diameter 100 mm (given).

Length (minimum 75 mm, maximum 100 mm) will probably be 80 mm and use will be made of the spacing collar E.

Cutter A

Diameter = 100 mm + 2(20 mm) = 140 mm.

Width is immaterial, would be about 25 mm (or about 15 mm if single angle).

Cutter C

Diameter = 100 mm + 2(10 mm) = 120 mm.
Width = 125 mm − 100 mm = 25 mm.

Cutter D

Minimum diameter = 100 mm + 2(20 mm) = 140 mm.

Minimum width = 2(95 mm − 80 mm) = 30 mm (or 15 mm if single angle).

It is highly probable a standard cutter would be used and due modification made to the width of the spacing collar F.

(c) 1. Use up-cut milling unless the machine has a backlash eliminator on the feed.
   2. Lock the knee.
   3. Lock the saddle.
   4. Maintain accurate adjustment on the table slides.
   5. Use cutters with helical flutes if possible.
   6. Select helices so that thrust is directed to spindle nose.
   7. Use key in arbor, do not rely on friction of collars.
   8. Place overarm supports as near to cutters as possible.
   9. Rigidly clamp the workpiece.
   10. Adjust speed, feed and depth of cutter if necessary.

(Reduction of speed usually helps, but feed and depth of cutter may have to be adjusted either way, depending upon geometry of cut.)

7.11   The component shown in Fig. 7.11a is finish machined except for the three 6/6·1 mm slots. Describe with the aid of neat sketches how these slots may be machined parallel to the axis of the 18 mm diameter hole, using a horizontal milling machine. It is important that the method of setting and clamping the component be clearly shown, together with the means adopted to ensure that all linear dimensions are within the limits indicated on the diagram. (w.j.e.c.)

The limits on the slots should allow the use of standard 6 mm side and face cutters, but this will depend on the condition of the machine and the diameters of the cutters. Three cutters of equal diameter should be selected, and tried independently for size by cutting slots in a block of lead. If standard cutters cannot provide sufficient accuracy, interlocking cutters could be used or standard side and face cutters of 5 mm width, cutting sides of the slots separately. The cutters may have to be ground to a common diameter. The size of actual slots cut should be noted and used in the calculations for the width of suitable collars. Sufficient accuracy may be obtained with standard collars of 14 mm width, but it may be necessary to make collars, or build-up extra width with shims. The gang assembly should be tried by cutting a block of lead to check the spacing. The gang assembly is left mounted on the arbor if correct.

An 18 mm test mandrel should be inserted in the bore. Under normal circumstances clamping should be as near to the cutting as possible. However, this particular detail has sufficient rigidity to be clamped only on the 20 mm flanges, using simple strap clamps as

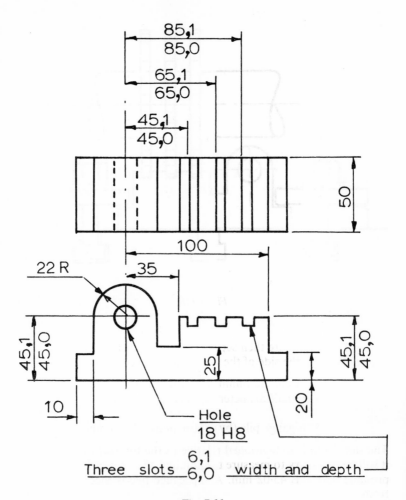

Fig. 7.11a

shown in Fig. 7.11b. There should be no need to clamp in the 13 mm channel. The initial clamping is light. The distance between the mandrel and cutter side is then checked with feeler gauges at both ends of the mandrel and when the mandrel is in correct alignment with the table travel, the clamping is tightened securely. The setting should be checked after clamping.

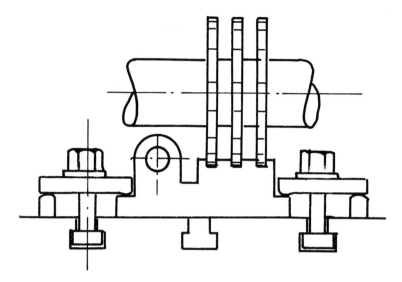

Fig. 7.11b

The cutters are then set relative to the component with a slip gauge pile from the side of the first cutter to the side of the mandrel.

Nominal mid-limit to centre   = 45·05 mm
Less half diameter of mandrel = 9 mm

Slip gauge pile (by subtraction) = 36·05 mm

The slot depth is dimensioned relative to the top surface and hence it will be necessary to measure the nominal 45 mm dimension. Let us presume that it is 45·02 mm. A slip gauge pile is then constructed from

Nominal height of face = 45·02 mm
Mid-limit of slop depth = 6·05 mm

Slip gauge pile   = 38·97 mm

The table height is adjusted until the slip gauge pile locates between the table surface and the cutting edges of the milling cutters at their lowest point of rotation. The cutter settings are shown in Fig. 7.11c.

177

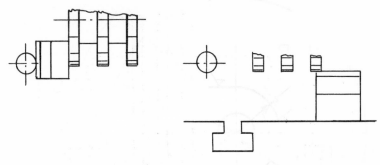

Fig. 7.11c

When all settings are made, non-moving sides are locked and all three slots cut with one pass.

Note: For this particular question a suitable method depends mainly upon the accuracy of the machine available. The method given is probably safest for any machine, but on a high quality machine in good condition sufficient accuracy may be available to use dial movements on the machine and to cut the slots one at a time. If more than one component is required, however, the gang milling method described would almost certainly be used.

7.12   The pawl (Fig. 7.12a) is to have the profile machined by milling where indicated thus ∇. With the aid of sketches describe the setting up and machining on a vertical machine. You may assume that standard ancillary equipment is available and that the 15 mm hole and the 75 mm radius have already been machined.   (Y.C.F.E.)

The milling can be undertaken using a 20 mm slot drill, in order to obtain the 10 mm radii. Setting and machining are facilitated with the aid of a rotary table. The rotary table is located on the machine table with its tenons, and then clamped to the table of the milling machine. A rotating dial indicator is used to align the machine spindle with the centre of the rotary table and then feed dials on the machine are set at zero.

The central hole of the rotary table can be used to position the component, with a 15 mm test mandrel. The component would be clamped with four strap clamps on to parallels, as the component must lie above the face of the table. It would assist if the design of the

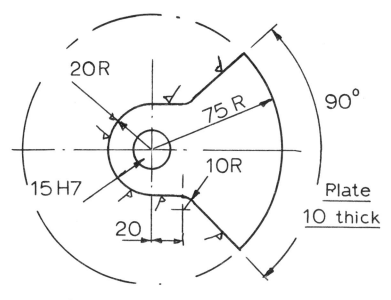

Fig. 7.12a

Fig. 7.12b–g

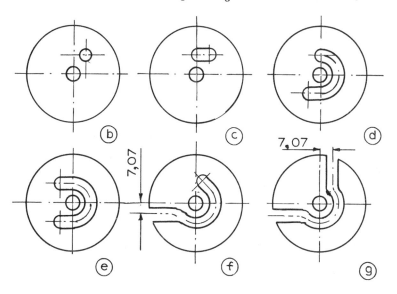

rotary table allowed a central clamp through the 15 mm hole of the component with a spacing washer of the same height as the parellels. The clamping is shown in Fig. 7.12h.

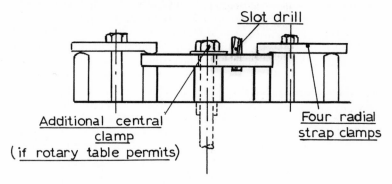

Fig. 7.12h

Since a slot drill cuts full diameter on its end, the table should be moved outwards 30 mm, leftwards 20 mm and a 20 mm hole should be machined in the disc by plunge cutting with the slot drill. The slot drill should not be withdrawn (Fig. 7.12b.) The table is now traversed 20 mm rightwards (Fig. 7.12c). The next feed is 180° clockwise of the rotary table (Fig. 7.12d). The next traverse is rightwards 20 mm (Fig. 7.12e) and the table is lowered to withdraw the slot drill.

The table is now traversed so that the centre of the cutter is 7·07 mm from the centre of the table, the rotary table indexed 45° clockwise and a cut taken from the outside to join up with the slot (Fig. 7.12f). The final cut is taken after the rotary table has been traversed so that the cutter is 7·07 mm from centre, and for the final cutter the saddle (not the table) would be traversed (Fig. 7.12g).

7.13   A pipe flange 150 mm outside diameter, 100 mm inside diameter and 20 mm thick is to have five equally spaced holes 15 mm diameter on a 130 mm pitch circle diameter. Explain clearly with the aid of sketches:

(a) How you would drill one flange.

(b) How you would drill 250 flanges.

(c) How you would inspect the 250 drilled flanges.

    Illustrate all the special tools you would require in parts (b) and (c).   (Y.C.F.E.)

(a) One flange would be produced by marking out, centre punching the holes and drilling on a single spindle drilling machine. The marking out would be accomplished with the aid of a surface plate, an angle block and a vernier height gauge fitted with a scribing point. The actual outside diameter would be found and the plate strapped to the angle plate. A datum dimension would be determined by touching the scribing point to the top of the flange, and, based on this, datum horizontal lines would be scribed. The angle plate would be turned through 90° and once more a datum height established on the height gauge. Using this datum the marking out would be completed as shown in Fig. 7.13a. The holes would be centre popped, and the plate drilled on a single spindle drilling machine.

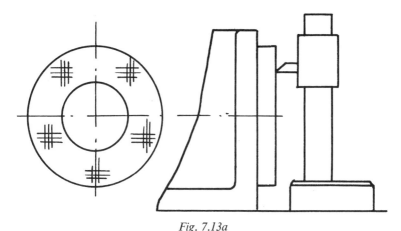

Fig. 7.13a

(b) For 250 flanges a jig should be used. Fig. 7.13b shows a suitable jig, constructed entirely of standard details except for the locating spigot. A flange is located on the spigot and clamped with the C-washer. Drilling would be undertaken on a single spindle drilling machine.

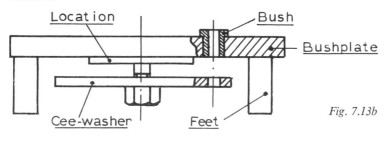

Fig. 7.13b

(c) For 250 flanges a receiver gauge should be used which duplicates the part of the component upon which the flange fits. It would consist of a simple disc with a spigot and recess, and carry six pegs accurately positioned on a 130 mm pitch circle diameter. The diameters of the spigot, recess and pegs depend upon the limits of the component. Inspection is undertaken by simply noting if the receiver gauge accepts a flange. This, in effect, is a 'go' check. The 'not-go' check depends upon the degree of checking considered necessary. It is highly probable in this case a 'not-go' check would not be considered necessary.

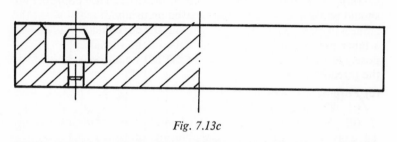

Fig. 7.13c

7.14   A standard 20 mm diameter hexagon-headed bolt could be headed by any one of the following methods:
(a) machining from the solid;
(b) permanently fixing a nut to the end of a bar;
(c) forging.
        For *each* method.
    (i)   state the form in which the material should be supplied;
    (ii)   state the kind of bolt or application which would justify the method;
    (iii)   describe briefly the heading process.   (C.G.L.I.)

        Assume a length of 100 mm.
(a) From the solid.
    (i)   Hexagon bar 30 mm across flats 125 mm long (alternatively round bar, diameter 36 mm, length 125 mm)
    (ii)   Where squareness of the underside of the head with the shank is important, e.g. for use in a counterbore or against a spot-face.
    (iii)   The head is virtually there if hexagon bar is used, but if not, flats could be cut by straddle milling, after turning, using an indexing arrangement.

(b) Securing a nut.

(i) Round bar of diameter 20 mm, 115 mm long; with a standard nut.

(ii) In an emergency where time for replacement has to be minimal, cheapness is important, load carrying is not unduly severe and there is absence of vibration. A typical example would be a replacement bolt in a structural framework of continental manufacture, where the workshop uses a preponderance of British manufactured articles and where squareness of the underside of the head to the shank is not important.

(iii) This method is the weakest of the three. The end of the rod should be threaded and the nut screwed on firmly. It may be that this alone will provide sufficient strength, but the nut could be pinned with a taper pin through the opposing flats, or the thread could be purposely left long and riveted over or the nut could be tackwelded to the thread.

(c) Forging.

(i) 20 mm black bar, 150 mm long.

(ii) Where strength is important and where vibration is present, e.g. a bolt securing a portion of a vibrating conveyor.

(iii) Heat about half the length of the rod to forging heat of about 1250°C. Commence upsetting by placing heated end on anvil, grip with tongs and striking other end. Reheat, upset to roughly round head form. Reheat, form hexagon by swaging, rotating at intervals to bring to hexagon form, occasionally flattening head as hexagon forms. Reheat, use hole in swage block and flatten to bring underside of head square with shank.

7.15(a) Explain clearly why it is easier to solder a copper component than a steel one. State in what form steel plate is supplied for soldering. (b) A sleeve is brazed on to a shaft. On what factors does the strength of the joint depend? (c) What are the relative merits of resin and zinc chloride (killed spirits) as soldering fluxes? (Y.C.F.E.)

(a) Soldered joints depend for their strength upon the alloying of the solder with the metals being joined. The usual type of solder, tinsmith's solder, is an alloy of tin and lead. The tin in the solder readily alloys with copper, but less readily with steel. Consequently it is easier to solder a copper component than one of steel.

Tin is easily soldered because the solder readily alloys with

*   183 the tin. Soldered joints do not have great mechanical strength, and if steel *has* to be soldered, coating the steel with tin and using the steel in the form of tinplate usually proves satisfactory.

(b) The strength of a brazed joint between a sleeve and a shaft will depend upon:
1. the materials of which the shaft and bush are made, and whether or not the brazing heat has affected these materials;
2. the cleanliness of the parts before brazing;
3. selection of the correct brazing spelter;
4. location of parts during brazing;
5. the clearance between the sleeve and the shaft (during the brazing, not at room temperature). Too close a fit prevents the brazing spelter from being drawn into the joint by capillary flow. Too great a clearance reduces the capillary effect;
6. the use of a suitable flux;
7. the presence of non-oxidizing conditions during brazing;
8. removal of flux residues after brazing;
9. the degree of embrittlement of the materials, particularly by hydrogen, sulphur and phosphorus.

(c) Soldering fluxes,
1. minimize the oxidation of the surfaces being joined, and the oxidation of the solder;
2. dissolve the oxides formed before and during the soldering; and
3. promote the free flowing of the solder.

'Killed spirits' effectively performs all these functions, but the water evaporates during soldering leaving a residue. This residue has a tendency to absorb water and form a very corrosive solution. There is no practical method of neutralizing the residue, it is usually removed by thorough washing. A resin flux will also perform the functions of a soldering flux but not so effectively as killed spirits, although the addition of certain organic compounds increase its effectiveness. The residue, however, does not absorb water and is non-corrosive. The flux will almost always be selected according to whether or not the flux residue can be removed. Complex electrical wiring which has to be soldered requires a resin flux, tinplate vessels are generally soldered with a flux of killed spirits.

7.16 Sketch any simple assembly suitable for joining together by brazing, and give the following information about it.
(a) Of what material is each part of the assembly made?

(b) What is the approximate composition and melting point of the spelter of filler metal?
(c) How are the parts located or held to ensure correct position after brazing?
(d) How is a suitable temperature obtained?
(e) How does one know whether the joint is sound?   (C.G.L.I.)

(a) The fork assembly shown in Fig. 7.16.

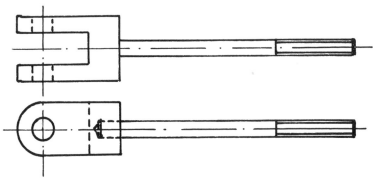

Fig. 7.16

Both portions are of mild steel, such as En 3b. In particular the rod should not be made of a high sulphur free cutting steel, as the presence of sulphur prevents a sound joint.

(b) The spelter could be a 55/45 copper/zinc alloy melting at a temperature of a little under 900°C, with borax used as a flux.

(c) One location is the fit of the mating diameters, which has to be carefully controlled. Too great a clearance, or too small a clearance, prevents a suitable capillary action drawing the molten spelter into the joint. Endwise location can be obtained using a dowel through fork end and rod.

(d) A suitable temperature is obtained by heating the brazing location with an oxy-coal gas blowpipe flame.

(e) There are three methods which could be used. Soundness should not be left to one single test.
1. A visual inspection of the joint—if a circlip of spelter had been used, the spelter should have run into the joint and not along the rod.
2. By tapping the assembly—a dull sound indicates an unsound

joint, a bell-like ring indicates a sound joint.
3. Mechanical testing—by applying a tensile load of say twice the value the assembly will meet in practice.

7.17 In manufacturing a simple bracket, a piece of mild steel strip 40 mm wide and 3 mm thick has to be bent to a right angle. There is serious and persistent cracking at the bend.
(a) Give three possible reasons for this trouble.
(b) Outline and explain the instructions which should be given in order to prevent the trouble in each case.   (C.G.L.I.)

(a) Three possible reasons could be:
1. Too small a radius inside the bend.
2. Material being of an unsuitable composition for a bending process.
3. Material being in an unsuitable condition for a bending process.
    (Other reasons could be the manner in which the bending is performed, variations in metal thickness and initial imperfections of the surface.)

(b) When a bending operation is performed, if the inside bend radius is too small, very little compression occurs inside the bend while considerable extension occurs on the outer surface. As a general guide, if T is the thickness of the material, the inside bend radius should not be less than T for material suitable for forming, or $2T$ with other qualities of steel. Increasing the bend radius will certainly overcome the trouble.
    If there are limitations in the maximum bend radius, it is necessary to pay attention to the material. There are many qualities of mild steel, and in order to minimize the cracking it is necessary to keep the carbon content as low as possible; a steel such as En 2 should be specified, rather than En 1 or En 3.
    In addition to the composition, steel is supplied in various conditions. Cracking could be due to incorrect quality of material, such as a bright mild steel in the 'as-rolled' condition. The material should be in the softest possible condition and bright mild steel in the as-rolled condition has a low ductility value.
    The instructions which should be given are:
1. The inside bend radius should be not less than 3 mm, preferably 5 mm.
2. The material should be En 2.

3. The material should be in the C.R.C.A. condition (cold rolled, close annealed).
4. The bending should be performed so that bending is uniformly progressive, e.g. in vee-bending tools in a hand press, on a folding machine or on a bending jig.

7.18   Three common causes of industrial accidents are:
(a) working in an unsafe environment;
(b) working in an unsafe manner;
(c) failure to provide suitable protective clothing or equipment.

   Give an example due to each of these causes and explain how each might have been avoided.   (C.G.L.I.)

(a) Unsafe environment.

   A bruise, a cut, or even a fracture caused by a collapsing pile of randomly stacked heavy components.

   These could be avoided by using stacking fixtures whose design ensures that stacking is stable and that components cannot be fortuitously dislodged. A typical example would be the stacking of heavy gear wheel blanks. The stacking fixture could be designed around a heavy three-point supported base with vertical rods whose length limits the number of blanks which can be stored on top of each other. An alternative method would be to use containers. Operators should be encouraged to avoid loose piling of products by having suitably designed storage equipment readily available.

(b) Unsafe manner.

   Damage to a finger, such as crushing, when changing a belt on a machine tool and the start button is pressed, either inadvertently by the person changing the belt or carelessly by someone at the machine.

   If a portion of the machine has to be moved to get at the belt, such as a door to be opened, or a guard removed, a simple micro-switch should be fitted which automatically cuts off the power supply if the door is opened or the guard removed. If such safety precautions are not available, care should be taken not to rely on machine controls themselves to be 'off'. The isolating switch, situated preferably some distance from the machine, should also be switched off.

(c) Lack of protective clothing.

   Damage to the eye, even as severe as loss of sight, by a foreign body entering the eye at high velocity.

This accident could arise in circumstances where brittle materials are subjected to blows or undue pressure. A typical example would be chipping at a concrete floor, using a hammer and chisel, to make the holes for the foundation bolts for machine tools. Such an accident could probably be avoided if goggles were worn whose lenses were manufactured of a suitable quality of material.

Certain modern transparent plastics are a considerable improvement on common glass.

7.19 The effects of stress and strain on materials are sometimes unwisely ignored in the workshop. Give an example in each of the following to show typical practical cases of overloading or incorrect loading, explaining the nature of the loading and the stresses produced:
(a) in which damage to machines or equipment may result;
(b) in which there is no visible effect, but inaccurate work may result;
(c) in which personal danger may result.   (U.E.I.)

(a) Using too great a torque in tightening a bolt with a spanner. Excessive torque loading produces excessive shear stress which could damage the bolt by shearing the head from the shank. Wherever possible, in particular with small bolts, a torque recording spanner should be used and recommended torques applied.

(b) Not adjusting the tailstock when longitudinal turning causes the work to expand, and the length/diameter relationship of the work-piece is that of a slender strut. This is often supplemented by excessive radial force of the cutting action. There is usually no noticeable effect, but excessive compressive force (caused by restricted expansion on a slender strut causes it to deflect by bowing. The radial force imposes an additional bending stress. The axis of the workpiece no longer being a straight line, inaccurate non-parallel work will result.

(c) Milling flat surfaces on long thin components with upcut milling, together with inefficient clamping. The loadings imposed by clamping and cutting should be directed so that they tend to bed the workpiece more firmly on to the table or into the fixture. If the clamping were to fail and the work leave the location when cutting is in process it could easily cause personal damage to the operator.

Upcut milling produces a combination of forces, but the one component which is being considered in this case is the one which tends to lift the work from its seating. Clamping, in order to provide a clear surface, may well be at the sides, and here, as in the previous example, we can have the bowing of a strut supplemented by a force amplifying the deflection.

The machining should be by climb milling and the clamping should have a component which tends to bed the work more firmly in its location.

CHAPTER 8

Workshop Materials

The questions in this chapter will be of use to readers who are preparing for examinations other than T2, such as the first year of a technological B.Sc. or O2 Workshop Technology.

8.1   Distinguish between grey cast iron and the malleable irons. State how each material is produced, its characteristics and common uses in engineering.

A grey iron casting is obtained by melting pig iron in a foundry cupola and pouring into a sand mould. The grey iron casting has iron as its major constituent and will also contain between 2% and 4% of carbon, mainly uncombined in the form of free graphite. Depending upon the pig iron used and the melting arrangements in the cupola (selected by considering the intended use of the article), a grey iron casting will contain up to 3% of silicon, up to 1% of manganese, up to 0·5% of phosphorus and up to 0·5% of sulphur. A grey cast iron forms sound castings, is very strong in compression, is easy to machine and has excellent vibration-damping characteristics. It is a brittle material, weak in tension, bending and shear, and has no well-defined yield point or modulus of elasticity. It is much used for basic structures of machine tools and structural members loaded in compression, such as bases of press tools. A high phosphorus grey cast iron pours very easily, is very cheap but is a low quality cast iron; it is used for covers of switch boxes and rainwater goods, which are cheap products requiring little or no machining and call for no particularly good physical characteristics.

A malleable iron is obtained by intentionally producing a white cast iron product of roughly the same composition as grey cast iron, the difference being that a white cast iron is one in which the carbon is mainly combined. The castings are then heated in suitable containers with other materials. The temperature is slowly brought up to about 875°C, held at this temperature for 2–3 days followed by cooling for a further 2–3 days. If the castings are in contact with an

190

inert material such as mill scale, the combined carbon in the white cast iron decomposes into temper carbon and ferrite, and the appearance of the fracture of the resulting product leads to the name of 'blackheart malleable iron'. If the castings are in contact with an oxidizing substance, practically all the carbon is removed and the appearance of the fracture of the resulting product leads to the name of 'whiteheart malleable cast iron'. Malleable iron, of either type, is comparatively strong in tension, compression and shear, machines readily and in particular is much more resistant to shock loading than grey cast iron. It is commonly used where service conditions impose high impact stresses, cyclic loading and abusive treatment. It finds considerable usage in the form of castings used in the automobile industry (spring hangers), the cycle industry (frame junctions) and the agricultural industry (harvester details).

8.2(a) What is a plain carbon steel and how does it differ from an alloy steel?
(b) Distinguish between hypo-eutectoid and hyper-eutectoid steels.
(c) Plain carbon steels are divided into three main groups. Name these, giving the approximate carbon content for each group.
(d) Indicate how the mechanical properties of an untreated plain carbon steel change as the carbon content increases to 0·9%.

(a) A plain carbon steel is a steel whose mechanical properties are decided by the percentage of carbon which is present. An alloy steel is a steel in which an element or elements other than carbon have been deliberately introduced to confer special properties on that steel.

(b) The eutectoid composition of plain carbon steels occurs in the vicinity of 0·9% carbon. Steels with less than about 0·9% of carbon are known as hypo-eutectoid steels. Hyper-eutectoid steels contain more than about 0·9% of carbon.

(c) The classification is generally confined to the hypo-eutectoid steels, as follows:
1. low carbon steels—0·05% to about 0·30% carbon;
2. medium carbon steels—about 0·30% to about 0·60% carbon;
3. high carbon steels—over about 0·60% to about 0·9% carbon.
 The percentages of carbon must be considered approximate.
 Hyper-eutectoid steels with carbon in excess of 0·9% are high carbon steels, but these are used for special applications rather than general constructions and are more often referred to as cast steels,

tool steels or special high carbon steels.

(d) The tensile strength increases roughly linearly from about 35 kgf/mm² at 0·05% carbon to about 90 kgf/mm² at 0·9% carbon. The hardness value increases roughly linearly from about HB 100 at 0·05% carbon to about HB 200 at 0·9% carbon.

Ductility, as measured by an elongation value, decreases as the percentage of carbon increases.

Malleability, as measured by a reduction in area value, decreases as the percentage of carbon increases.

No comment is offered on toughness. There is no standard test for toughness which provides a numerical value. (An Izod impact test is carried out by subjecting a specimen to a blow but the results obtained from an Izod test are no measure of toughness.) Toughness is a matter of opinion and is usually acquired by subjecting the steel to a heat treatment rather than expecting it in the untreated steel.

8.3(a) What is a free-cutting steel? State the elements which are usually added to make a steel free-cutting, and describe how they give this property.
(b) Give the approximate composition of a plain case-hardening steel and an alloy case-hardening steel. What benefits are obtained by using the latter instead of the former?

(a) A free-cutting steel is a steel which contains an element which has been deliberately added to promote rapid machining. The element is normally either sulphur or lead.

If sulphur is the added element (such as with En 1b), the sulphur forms a brittle constituent with manganese. Manganese sulphide, being brittle, allows chip cracks to propagate and breaks chips into easily handled lengths. The manganese content of a free-cutting steel is higher than for a normal mild steel. For example:

En 1b (free-cutting steel)   0·3% to 0·6% S   1·0% to 1·4% Mn
En 3b (black mild steel)   0·06% (max)   1·0% (max)

Lead bearing steels are not normally included in basic B.S. specifications and are associated with particular industrial undertakings (e.g. Ledloy steels). The lead does not chemically combine with the other elements, being distributed throughout the mass as minute droplets. Once more chip cracks are propagated easily and the chips come off the tool in easily managed lengths.

(b)

	Plain C.H. steel (*En* 32)	*Alloy CH steel* (*En* 37)
Carbon	0·15% max	0·15% max
Silicon	0·25%	0·25%
Manganese	0·5%	0·5%
Sulphur	0·05% max	0·05% max
Phosphorus	0·05% max	0·05% max
Nickel	Nil	5%

It will be observed that the only difference is the nickel content. The purpose of adding the nickel is to strengthen the core ($50\ kgf/mm^2$ to $65\ kgf/mm^2$), and to deter grain growth during carburizing. If the carburizing is rapid, as occurs with a small component using cyanide as the carburizing medium, the use of nickel can occasionally eliminate the refining operation.

8.4(a) Which two elements are alloyed to form a brass?
(b) What are the differences (i) in composition, (ii) in uses, of an 'alpha' and an 'alpha-beta' brass?
(c) What is meant by the work-hardening of a cartridge brass used in presswork and how is this work-hardening corrected if the components are to be subjected to further severe presswork?

(a) A brass is an alloy whose major constituents are copper and zinc. Minor proportions of elements such as lead and tin may be included to promote special properties, but the alloy is essentially one of copper and zinc.

(b) An alpha brass is an alloy where the proportion of zinc does not exceed about 38%. The brass is ductile and consequently is used for cold-rolled sheets, wire, tube and cold pressings. A typical alpha brass is cartridge brass (70% copper, 30% zinc). Its name indicates its use, being a very suitable material for deep-drawing cartridge cases.
   An alpha-beta brass is an alloy of copper and zinc where the proportion of zinc lies between about 38% and about 47%. The appearance of the beta constituent is associated with increased strength at the expense of ductility. An alpha-beta brass does not lend itself to cold-working, but is readily hot-worked by rolling, extrusion and hot-pressing. It is readily machined, the machineability being even more improved by the addition of lead. A typical alpha-beta brass is Muntz metal (60% copper, 40% zinc), which is used for

the production of low pressure water fittings by hot-pressing and, when lead-bearing, for the rapid production of screws and nuts.

(c) Work-hardening is an increase in surface hardness due to the distortion of crystal grains by cold-working. It can be corrected by annealing. The pressed components are heated to a temperature above the recrystallization temperature, this being decided by the composition of the brass. The broken and distorted grains form new grains of regular and large size. After soaking for a suitable time the rate of cooling is immaterial.

8.5(a) What is the main difference between a brass and a bronze?

(b) State (i) the composition, and (ii) two common uses, of a bronze used in engineering.

(c) What is the general effect of adding a small proportion of (i) phosphorus, (ii) lead, to a bronze?

(a) A brass is generally considered to be an alloy, the major constituent being copper, the next most important constituent being zinc.

A bronze is generally considered to be an alloy, the major constituent being copper, the next most important constituent being tin. There are two important alloys which include the word bronze in their title, but in each case the presence of tin is fortuitous rather than intentional. Aluminium bronze and manganese bronze, in the opinion of many authorities, are misnomers and should be considered to be high-tensile brasses.

(b) (i) A bronze commonly used in engineering is colloquially known as 'eighty-five, three-fives' and consists of 85% of copper, with 5% each of tin, zinc and lead. This is a good general purpose bronze which has tended to replace the traditional admiralty gun metal (88% copper, 10% tin, 2% zinc) because of its improved machining qualities.

(ii) It is used for low pressure pipe fittings and small pump castings where reasonable corrosion resistance is desired.

(c) (i) Phosphorus has two effects depending on the proportion remaining in the final casting. If the proportion is very small, often only a trace, the phosphorus improved fluidity when casting. If the phosphorus ranges from about 0·05% to 0·25% as in a phosphor-bronze, the phosphorus will have formed cuboids which resist wear and can carry heavy leads; consequently, it contributes valuable properties to bearing materials.

(ii) Lead is distributed throughout a bronze as globules. It allows chip cracks to propagate easily and hence the addition of lead improves machining qualities.

8.6   State, with reasons, a suitable material for the manufacture of each of the following, giving the approximate composition:
(a) a brass for deep pressed containers;
(b) a brass for small machined bolts;
(c) a steel for general purpose cutting tools on a capstan lathe;
(d) a bronze for the impeller of a sea-water pump.   (U.L.C.I.)

(a) Admiralty brass.

Copper and zinc in the proportion of 7 to 3, with 1% of tin.

Material is ductile, the addition of tin to the basic cartridge brass (70% copper, 30% zinc) gives improved resistance to corrosion, renders the material less prone to season cracking, and could possibly lessen the number of, or even eliminate, interstage annealings.

(b) Free cutting brass.

61·5% copper, 35·5% zinc, 3% lead.

This material is basically a leaded Muntz metal, the addition of lead gives the material the highest machineability rating of the brasses.

(c) High speed steel (18–4–1)

An alloy steel whose major alloying elements are tungsten 18%, chromium 4% and vanadium 1%, together with iron, carbon, silicon, manganese and the minimum of sulphur and phosphorus.

The material is a general purpose material, cheaper than a 'super H.S.S.' (18–4–1–1 or 22–4–1), and retains its hardness at the elevated temperatures obtained when cutting operations are performed, such as capstan lathe turning.

(d) Admiralty gun metal.

85% copper, 10% tin, 2% zinc.

Produces sound castings and has excellent resistance to salt-water corrosion. Machineability could be improved by addition of lead, but this has to be balanced against a lower resistance to corrosion. If some corrosion resistance can be sacrificed in order to obtain improved machineability, 'eighty-five, three fives' (85% copper, 5% each of tin, zinc and lead) would prove suitable.

8.7(a) What are the characteristic properties of aluminium?
(b) Aluminium alloys may be classified as (i) wrought alloys, (ii) casting alloys. What alloying elements are associated with each class? Give one example of each class stating the composition, properties and uses.

(a) Pure aluminium is a very soft metallic element with a specific weight of about one-third of that of steel. Aluminium is very malleable, is easily formed, has excellent resistance to corrosive attack by industrial and marine atmospheres, chemicals and food products, is a good conductor of heat, a good conductor of electricity and a good reflector of heat.

Aluminium is too soft to find general engineering usage in its pure state, except as a cladding. It forms an impervious oxide skin which, having formed, prevents further oxidation. Its main use is as an alloying material. If aluminium is the major constituent, the alloys are characterized by their lightness, being about one-third of the specific weight of steel. Some alloys can be heat treated to produce physical properties in excess of some steels, resulting in very high strength–weight ratios.

(b) It is extremely difficult to associate any particular elements with each class. The most common elements alloyed with aluminium are silicon, iron, copper, manganese, magnesium, chromium, nickel and zinc. They can be used singly, or in combination, for both wrought and casting alloys. Some alloys are extremely complex, with as many as six elements intentionally present in addition to those present as impurities. As a wide (and a very wide) generalization silicon can be associated with casting alloys and magnesium or copper with wrought alloys, but some casting alloys do not contain silicon and some wrought alloys do not contain copper.

The number of aluminium alloys are legion, each one being developed for a particular use and often marketed under a trade name which in time becomes common usage. A casting alloy used for certain die cast pistons has 12% silicon, 1·5% nickel, 1% copper, 1% magnesium. It has a tensile strength, when chill cast, of about half of that of mild steel. An alloy used for certain structural sections on aircraft contains 4% copper, 1% magnesium, 0·5% silicon and 0·5% manganese, and in the heat-treated condition has a tensile strength about equal to that of mild steel with an elongation of 10%.

8.8(a) List four materials commonly used for cutting tools for machining operations, and the usual type of cutting for which each is particularly suited.
(b) State, and briefly describe, three different methods for the economical usage of expensive cutting tool materials.
(c) State the composition of a typical high speed steel.
(d) Why has high speed steel superseded high carbon tool steel as a general purpose cutting tool medium?

(a) 1. High carbon tool steel, correctly treated, is harder than H.S.S. at ordinary room temperatures, but softens rapidly as the cutting temperature increases and is therefore used when high temperatures are not generated when relatively slow cutting, e.g. hand tapping and guillotine shearing.

2. High speed steel is used as a general purpose cutting tool material where cutting temperatures are substantially in excess of those encountered with high carbon tool steels, because H.S.S. does not soften significantly at the elevated temperatures obtained in the conventional machining of commonly used work materials. Typical applications are drilling, machine tapping, machine reaming and centre lathe turning of mild steel.

3. Cemented carbides are used when high rates of stock removal are required, and the very high cutting temperatures would affect even high speed steel. It is especially suitable for cutting non-ductile materials and harder alloy steels with high rates of feed, high cutting speeds and large depths of cut.

4. Ceramics are used in certain restricted circumstances when the amount of stock removal is relatively low but a fine finish is required and cutting of the work material has a very abrasive effect on the cutting tool, e.g. turning laminated plastics.

Note: Two other materials in even more restricted use are stellite, for highly abrasive and intermittent cutting, and industrial diamonds, for very low stock removal but a high degree of surface finish.

(b) Buttwelding, often used with large drills, where the cutting portion of high speed steel is buttwelded to a carbon steel shank.

Tipped tools, such as lathe tools, where a carbide tip is brazed into a seating on a carbon steel shank.

Inserted teeth, such as milling cutters, where teeth are mechanically gripped in a steel body.

(c) There are two main types of high speed steel. The most common is tungsten high speed steel, with about 18% tungsten, 4% chromium and 1% vanadium colloquially referred to as 18–4–1 high speed steel. A typical molybdenum high speed steel, colloquially known as substitute 66, has 6% each of molybdenum and tungsten.

(d) The presence of tungsten in a high speed steel gives to that steel the property of 'red-hardness', which is a capacity of the steel to retain hardness at elevated temperatures. High speed steels can therefore cut at higher speeds than high carbon tool steels. They are still capable of cutting even when the tool tip approaches red heat. At such temperatures high carbon tool steels soften due to tempering, and are often completely unable to cut. As the need to cheapen production has led to increased rates of metal removal, involving higher temperatures, so the use of high carbon steel has decreased in favour of high speed steel. (The trend is continuing with an increased usage of cemented carbides as against high speed steels, but the carbides may have a tendency to fail by cratering.)